Steins

The Official
Collector's Guide To
Anheuser-Busch
Steins

V O L U M E   T W O

Anheuser-Busch, Inc.

Original Design and
Art Direction by
Phoenix Creative,
Saint Louis, Missouri.
Photography by
David McCarthy.

Volume Two produced
by Direct Impact, Inc.,
Saint Louis, Missouri.
Photography by
Tony Smith, Anthony &
Bartz Photography

ISBN 0-9637395-1-4

Table of Contents

ANHEUSER-BUSCH has enjoyed a long and distinguished history. In 1869 Adolphus Busch set out to brew a quality product, making the best beer he could the only way he knew how. He believed that brewing great beer was an art and that only the finest would do. ❧ Although he may not have said it, he was guided by a promise Anheuser-Busch proudly makes today, *Somebody Still Cares About Quality.*

THE EARLY DAYS were not always easy, but the young company grew. Through it all, years of hard work and unwavering dedication, Anheuser-Busch was driven by one guiding principle: a commitment to quality. ❧ This commitment went into every aspect of brewing, from ingredients and equipment to people and promotion. The company worked hard to be innovative, always looking toward the future. This striving to be the best eventually came to fruition when Anheuser-Busch became the world's largest brewer. ❧ After 38 years, Anheuser-Busch is still the world's largest brewer and is still dedicated to its commitment to quality.

THE HISTORY of the beer stein begins more than 500 years ago. Although people have been drinking beer since the days of Ancient Egypt, it wasn't until the 15th Century that steins came into widespread use. ❧ At that time, after decades of the Black Plague, scientists concluded that the disease was spread by flies. As a result, laws were passed requiring public houses to serve beer and other beverages in lidded containers. So to keep out the flies and still allow drinking with one hand, the beer stein was born.

FOR THE NEXT few hundred years, laws requiring lidded steins remained, even long after the need was gone. During this time, the art of stein-making grew. Craftsmen from all over Europe traveled to Germany, developing fine steins into an art form. ❧ By the mid 1700s, the manufacturing technology greatly advanced, making steins more diverse and more affordable. No longer were steins only for the rich—the middle class was buying and using them, too. And because steins were a part of everyday life, the common people's tastes were reflected in the art and the craftsmanship. It is this style of steins which grew in popularity and remains desirable to collectors in modern times.

DEVELOPING AND COLLECTING steins has remained popular through the ages. Since the mid 1970s, this vintage art form has enjoyed a modern renaissance with collecting growing dramatically. ∾ As the world's largest brewer, Anheuser-Busch has been at the forefront of the movement, commissioning its first steins in the 1950s and 1960s for purchase by the general public. ∾ This book proudly chronicles the history of Anheuser-Busch collectible steins, which have been guided by that same commitment to excellence begun over a century ago, proving once again that *Somebody Still Cares About Quality.*

THIS SECOND EDITION of our Official Collector's Guide provides the most complete information available on the vast array of steins introduced by Anheuser-Busch over the years. ∾ Included are steins in the Collectors Series, item numbers beginning with CS; Special Event Series, beginning with SO and N; the Licensed Gerz Series, beginning with GM and GL; and Collectors Club steins, beginning with CB. Edition quantities listed are the maximum that can be produced, but actual production may be lower. ∾ Over 100 steins have been added to those in Volume One and information has also been updated for several items.

WE WOULD LIKE TO THANK the collectors who provided information that helped make this book a more comprehensive history of our steins. However, documentation for certain steins remains lost and verification of other documents has not yet been possible. ∾ We will continue our efforts to gather information for future editions and would like to continue the helpful dialogue we have begun with our collectors. If you have any additional information regarding Anheuser-Busch steins, please send it to:

> *Promotional Products Group*
> *Steins & Collectibles*
> *2700 South Broadway*
> *St. Louis, MO 63118 USA*

1.

2.

3.

4.

5.

7.

6.

8.

9.

10.

11.

12.

Stein Terminology

THE BASIC DESIGN of the beer stein consists of individually crafted parts or "mountings." These parts are created by artists and craftsmen ranging from metalsmiths to sculptors. Whether the body shape is conical, cylindrical, flatwall or modern, all steins share a number of characteristics. Virtually every stein has a base, but these bases come in a wide range of styles. All lidded steins have a thumbrest, but the designs are often quite stylized and unique. The photograph at left labels the most common stein terminology. Most of the twelve components are found only on lidded steins.

1. *Thumbrest*	7. *Handle*
2. *Tang*	8. *Lid*
3. *Hinge & Pin*	9. *Flange*
4. *Shank*	10. *Lidring*
5. *Strap Support*	11. *Body*
6. *Strap*	12. *Footring*

Limited edition steins are numbered and marked by the manufacturer by varying methods. Frequently, this marking consists of an identifying stamp or decal on the bottom. In other instances, the manufacturer identifies the stein by means of a crest or medallion. Anheuser-Busch limited edition collectible steins are marked in two manners. Ceramarte individually numbers each stein in gold on the bottom stamp. Until recently, Gerz numbered its steins by means of a pewter medallion attached to a leather fob which hangs from the stein's handle. Then, in 1994, Gerz began numbering its steins on the bottom stamp.

The History of Ceramarte

T HE HISTORY of Ceramarte begins in 1952 when Klaus and Maria Erdmuthe Schumacher moved from Germany to the small town of Rio Negrinho, Brazil. Their dream was to create the same type of high-quality ceramics similar to the ones so often produced in their native Germany. Klaus was an accomplished ceramist and Maria, an experienced ceramic model maker, designer and painter. They had the necessary background for success.

CERAMARTE PLANT, RIO NEGRINHO, BRAZIL

The Schumachers spent the first few years learning the language and preparing to start their business. During that time, the husband and wife team searched for usable raw materials, constructed a kiln and contacted prospective clients. Soon they were ready to open Ceramarte.

The first of Ceramarte's ceramics included art pieces, wall tiles, flower pots and beer steins. Although all the pieces were well-crafted, the beer steins were by far superior. The Schumachers decided to exclusively produce these ceramic steins, and soon afterward many local clubs and organizations became interested in the "promotional" steins.

SPECIAL DELIVERY SIGNATURE EDITION STEIN, ITEM NUMBER CS192SE

By 1963, Ceramarte had already produced one million promotional steins.

By the mid 1970s, the Schumachers were ready to take the next

1975 BUD MAN
STEIN, ITEM
NUMBER CS1

logical step. Klaus made a number of trips to the United States, exploring the international market. Eventually, Klaus received his first order. Not many years later, Ceramarte committed solely to the production of beer steins for the international market, mainly for companies in the United States.

PRESIDENT
ABRAHAM
LINCOLN
STEIN, ITEM
NUMBER
CS189

Over the last two decades, Ceramarte has expanded and modernized. The company has improved its product by specializing in a fine grain stoneware body which is fired at the high temperature of 2380 degrees. This process creates the fine finish which is a Ceramarte trademark. In addition, Ceramarte has worked hard to keep up with growing customer demands. The most recent example of this is Ceramarte's new capability of producing quality pewter lids for its steins.

In a history spanning more than 30 years, Ceramarte has constantly provided superior ceramic beer steins to customers and collectors all over the globe. That's why Ceramarte is recognized as the world's largest ceramic beer stein producer.

The History of Gerz

S.P. GERZ was founded over 100 years ago in Westerwald, a part of Sessenbach, Germany. This small town is in the heartland of an area known as the "Kannenbackerland" meaning baked jug or mug, or more commonly baked clay land. In the area, historians have found pottery from as early as The Bronze Age. Potters, called "Euler" (from the word "olla" meaning pot) first settled in the area in the 16th century. Soon, any craftsman interested in stoneware manufacturing came to this region. These artists brought with them special glazing and burning techniques, and quickly succeeded in making a clay product with extraordinary density and hardness.

A GERZ MASTER CRAFTSMAN REVIEWING STEINS.

Simon Peter Gerz, one of a dynamic group of young potters, founded S.P. Gerz in 1862. The small company began by producing Siegburg stoneware, known for its fine grey body with cobalt-blue and manganese-violet glaze. Gerz was an innovator, pioneering mechanized production. In 1884, Gerz was appointed as the Purveyor to the Dukes of Nassau.

In the mid 1970s, a new "Golden Era" of stein art began. Master modelers such as Edwin Breiden of

SANTA'S MAILBAG STEIN, ITEM NUMBER GM1

BILL ELLIOTT
STEIN, ITEM
NUMBER
CS196

Gerz started to introduce new designs produced by new techniques. Serious collectors quickly accepted these steins, initiating newer and better production methods. It was also during this time that Anheuser-Busch began what was to become its long-standing relationship with Gerz.

As the largest manufacturer of German steins, Gerz continues to promote the production of beer steins as an art form. Most recently, Gerz has developed the innovative processes of shallow relief and transfer decoration.

From its introduction of new technology to its continual advancement of quality collectible steins, Gerz has been and continues to be at the forefront of its industry. Much like Anheuser-Busch, S.P. Gerz has committed to being the best.

CHERUB
STEIN, ITEM
NUMBER
CS182

The Early Years

Nineteen seventy five marks the year Anheuser-Busch commissioned its first collectible steins. These early works, noted for their traditional designs and fine craftsmanship, include subject matters such as German tavern scenes, historic brewery scenes and traditional Anheuser-Busch symbols. As a group, these steins began Anheuser-Busch's commitment to introducing high-quality collectibles to stein enthusiasts around the globe. ∾

The Early Years

Contents of This Section

SIDE VIEW

DETAIL

ISSUE YEAR:
1976
EDITION QUANTITY:
Open
ITEM NUMBER:
CS3

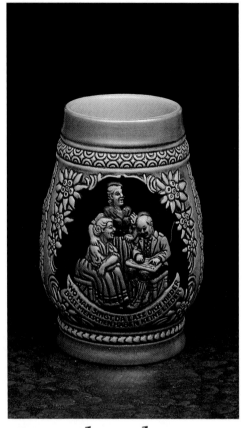

Katakombe

HEIGHT:
6″
ORIGIN:
Brazil
MANUFACTURER:
Ceramarte
MATERIAL:
Ceramic

Honoring the German tavern, this Katakombe stein is manufactured in relief with a rounded base shape. The detailed background includes a traditional German message and delicate edelweiss flowers. This is the unlidded version of CSL3.

DETAIL

Katakombe

Lidded

ISSUE YEAR:
1976
EDITION QUANTITY:
Open
ITEM NUMBER:
CSL3

Honoring the German tavern, this Katakombe stein is manufactured in relief with a rounded base shape. The detailed background includes a traditional German message and delicate edelweiss flowers. The stein lid and thumbrest are solid pewter.

HEIGHT:
7¾"
ORIGIN:
Brazil
MANUFACTURER:
Ceramarte
MATERIAL:
Ceramic
LID:
Pewter

SIDE VIEW

DETAIL

ISSUE YEAR:
1976
EDITION QUANTITY:
Open
ITEM NUMBER:
CS4

German Tavern Scene

HEIGHT:
7½"
ORIGIN:
Brazil
MANUFACTURER:
Ceramarte
MATERIAL:
Ceramic

This detailed stein features a festive German tavern scene against a deep cobalt blue background. The scene is framed in detailed relief design. German Tavern Scene is one of the earlier stein offerings.

SIDE VIEW

DETAIL

Senior Grande

Lidded

ISSUE YEAR:
1975
EDITION QUANTITY:
Open
ITEM NUMBER:
CSL4

This stein is reminiscent of many antique German steins. The impressive relief work fills the body and the local tavern scene is enhanced with colorful artistic highlights. This is the lidded version of cs6.

HEIGHT:
14″
ORIGIN:
Brazil
MANUFACTURER:
Ceramarte
MATERIAL:
Ceramic
LID:
Pewter

SIDE VIEW

DETAIL

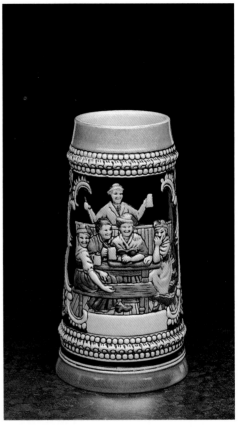

ISSUE YEAR:
1975
EDITION QUANTITY:
Open
ITEM NUMBER:
CS5

German Pilique

HEIGHT:
8¼"
ORIGIN:
Brazil
MANUFACTURER:
Ceramarte
MATERIAL:
Ceramic

This relief stein details a German village tavern scene complete with locals in traditional German costumes. The scene is set against a cobalt blue background and sculpted relief edges. This is the unlidded version of CSL5.

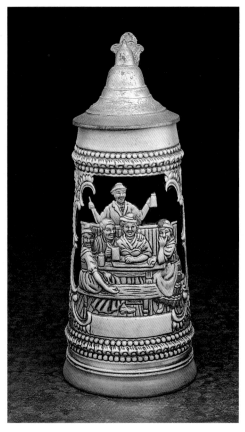

SIDE VIEW

DETAIL

German Pilique

Lidded

ISSUE YEAR:
1976
EDITION QUANTITY:
Open
ITEM NUMBER:
CSL5

This lidded stein details a German village tavern scene complete with locals in traditional German costumes. The scene is set against a cobalt blue background and sculpted relief edges. This 10¾" stein also features a solid pewter lid. This is the lidded version of cs5.

HEIGHT:
10¾"
ORIGIN:
Brazil
MANUFACTURER:
Ceramarte
MATERIAL:
Ceramic
LID:
Pewter

SIDE VIEW

DETAIL

ISSUE YEAR:
1977
EDITION QUANTITY:
Open
ITEM NUMBER:
CS6

Senior Grande

HEIGHT:
11″
ORIGIN:
Brazil
MANUFACTURER:
Ceramarte
MATERIAL:
Ceramic

This stein is reminiscent of many antique German steins. The impressive relief work fills the body and the local tavern scene is enhanced with colorful artistic highlights. This is the unlidded version of CSL4.

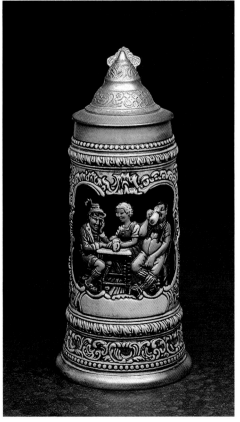

DETAIL

German Tavern Scene

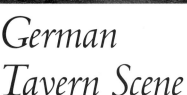

Lidded

ISSUE YEAR:
1975
EDITION QUANTITY:
Open
ITEM NUMBER:
CSL6

This lidded stein features a festive German tavern scene against a deep cobalt blue background. The scene is framed in detailed relief design. German Tavern Scene is one of the earlier stein offerings. This is the lidded version of CS4.

HEIGHT:
9½″
ORIGIN:
Brazil
MANUFACTURER:
Ceramarte
MATERIAL:
Ceramic
LID:
Pewter

SIDE VIEW

DETAIL

ISSUE YEAR:
1976
EDITION QUANTITY:
Open
ITEM NUMBER:
CSL7

Budweiser Centennial

Lidded

HEIGHT:
10˝
ORIGIN:
Brazil
MANUFACTURER:
Ceramarte
MATERIAL:
Ceramic
LID:
Pewter

This commemorative stein celebrates the 100-year anniversary of Budweiser, the world's largest selling beer. The 10˝ lidded stein has a solid pewter lid with decorative thumbrest and relief handle. The A&Eagle logo is featured in detailed relief on the center of the stein, with surrounding decorative border. This stein is the lidded version of cs13.

SIDE VIEW

DETAIL

U.S. Bicentennial

Lidded

ISSUE YEAR:
1976
EDITION QUANTITY:
Open
ITEM NUMBER:
CSL8

This patriotic stein commemorates the 200-year anniversary of the signing of America's Declaration of Independence. These immortal words are etched in relief across the stein, remembering that significant event in American History. Other memorable features of this stein include detailed artwork of the American Bald Eagle and a solid pewter lid.

HEIGHT:
10˝
ORIGIN:
Brazil
MANUFACTURER:
Ceramarte
MATERIAL:
Ceramic
LID:
Pewter

SIDE VIEW

DETAIL

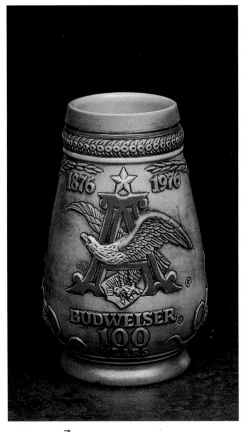

ISSUE YEAR:
1976
EDITION QUANTITY:
Open
ITEM NUMBER:
CS13

Budweiser Centennial

HEIGHT:
7½″
ORIGIN:
Brazil
MANUFACTURER:
Ceramarte
MATERIAL:
Ceramic

This commemorative relief stein celebrates the 100-year anniversary of Budweiser, the world's largest selling beer. The A&Eagle logo is the main focus, surrounded by relief border decorations. This stein is the unlidded version of CSL7.

SIDE VIEW

DETAIL

U.S. Bicentennial

ISSUE YEAR:
1976
EDITION QUANTITY:
Open
ITEM NUMBER:
CS14

T his patriotic stein commemorates the 200-year anniversary of the signing of America's Declaration of Independence. These immortal words are etched in relief across the stein, remembering this significant event in American History. Another memorable feature of this stein is the detailed artwork of the American Bald Eagle. This stein is the unlidded version of CSL8.

HEIGHT:
10˝
ORIGIN:
Brazil
MANUFACTURER:
Ceramarte
MATERIAL:
Ceramic

SIDE VIEW

DETAIL

ISSUE YEAR:
1976
EDITION QUANTITY:
Open
ITEM NUMBER:
CS22

Budweiser Centennial

Hofbrau Style

HEIGHT:
4¾″
ORIGIN:
Brazil
MANUFACTURER:
Ceramarte
MATERIAL:
Ceramic

This commemorative stein celebrates the 100-year anniversary of Budweiser, the world's largest selling beer. The antique wash on this half-liter stein gives it an old world feel while graphically representing the A&Eagle trademark, Budweiser logo and labels between the centennial dates 1876-1976.

SIDE VIEW

DETAIL

German Wine Set

ISSUE YEAR:
1976
EDITION QUANTITY:
Open
ITEM NUMBER:
CS32

This German Wine Set of seven pieces includes a full relief pitcher and six matching cups. Both the pitcher and cups have an intricate grape and leaf design.

HEIGHT:
6½″ Decanter
2½″ Cups
ORIGIN:
Brazil
MANUFACTURER:
Ceramarte
MATERIAL:
Ceramic

SIDE VIEW

DETAIL

ISSUE YEAR:
1976
EDITION QUANTITY:
Open
ITEM NUMBER:
CS37

St. Louis Decanter

HEIGHT:
11″
ORIGIN:
Brazil
MANUFACTURER:
Ceramarte
MATERIAL:
Ceramic
LID:
Ceramic

This brown and tan decanter highlights many of the famous Anheuser-Busch Brewery landmarks and traditions in the St. Louis area. The decanter's design includes illustrations of the Brewhouse, Stables and the Clydesdales eight-horse hitch. Same decanter included with the CS38 set.

SIDE VIEW

DETAIL

St. Louis Decanter Set

ISSUE YEAR:
1976
EDITION QUANTITY:
Open
ITEM NUMBER:
CS38

This brown and tan decanter, part of a seven-piece set, highlights many of the famous Anheuser-Busch Brewery landmarks and traditions in the St. Louis area. The decanter's design includes illustrations of the Brewhouse, Stables and the Clydesdales eight-horse hitch. Each of the six accompanying cups has the A&Eagle symbol across the front.

HEIGHT:
11˝ Decanter
3¼˝ Cups
ORIGIN:
Brazil
MANUFACTURER:
Ceramarte
MATERIAL:
Ceramic
LID:
Ceramic

SIDE VIEW

DETAIL

ISSUE YEAR:
Circa 1979
EDITION QUANTITY:
Open
ITEM NUMBER:
CS39

Würzburger

HEIGHT:
5″
ORIGIN:
West Germany
MANUFACTURER:
Unknown
MATERIAL:
Ceramic

This half-liter design carries the Würzburger Hofbrau name on front. The logo depicts a beautiful castle encircled by a frame and accented with gold colors and stalks of wheat.

A&Eagle Steins

The unique A&Eagle design is the widely recognized quality symbol of Anheuser-Busch, Inc. This trademark, still in use today, was first displayed on the company's beer products in 1872. After more than one hundred years, the A&Eagle has remained an unwavering symbol of quality. These illustrations artfully depict the intricate A&Eagle on an assortment of detailed steins. ᴖ

A&Eagle Steins

Contents of This Section

SIDE VIEW

DETAIL

ISSUE YEAR:
1976
EDITION QUANTITY:
Open
ITEM NUMBER:
CS2

A&Eagle

HEIGHT:
8″
ORIGIN:
Brazil
MANUFACTURER:
Ceramarte
MATERIAL:
Ceramic

The A&Eagle trademark is depicted on this alluring ceramic stein. The century-old symbol is featured in full color and is enhanced by a cobalt blue background. The famous Clydesdales eight-horse hitch runs around the bottom of the stein in a finely detailed relief motif. Anheuser-Busch and St. Louis, Missouri are etched into the top band of this stein.

SIDE VIEW

DETAIL

A&Eagle

Lidded

ISSUE YEAR:
1976
EDITION QUANTITY:
Open
ITEM NUMBER:
*Issued Under Two
Item Numbers:*
CSL2
CS28

The A&Eagle trademark is depicted on this alluring ceramic stein. The century-old symbol, featured in full color, is enhanced by a cobalt blue background and relief border design. The famous Clydesdales eight-horse hitch runs around the bottom of the stein in finely detailed relief. Anheuser-Busch and St. Louis, Missouri are etched into the top band of this stein.

HEIGHT:
10″
ORIGIN:
Brazil
MANUFACTURER:
Ceramarte
MATERIAL:
Ceramic
LID:
Pewter

SIDE VIEW

DETAIL

A&Eagle

ISSUE YEAR:
1976
EDITION QUANTITY:
Open
ITEM NUMBER:
CS26

HEIGHT:
5½″
ORIGIN:
Brazil
MANUFACTURER:
Ceramarte
MATERIAL:
Ceramic

This unique half-liter stein is crafted in detailed relief and shaped to resemble a beer barrel. The A&Eagle trademark and Budweiser logos fill the front of this vintage stein.

Holiday Steins

Collectors are invited to celebrate the holiday season with this beautiful selection of seasonal steins. Included in the Holiday section is the long-running Budweiser Holiday Series as well as a number of special limited-edition signature steins.

All of the original artwork is lavishly illustrated with minute detail and rich color, making each one a delightful addition to any collection. ❧

Holiday Steins

Contents of This Section

SIDE VIEW

DETAIL

ISSUE YEAR:
1980
EDITION QUANTITY:
Open
ITEM NUMBER:
CS19
SERIES ORDER:
First

Budweiser Champion Clydesdales

HEIGHT:
4¾"
ORIGIN:
Brazil
MANUFACTURER:
Ceramarte
MATERIAL:
Ceramic

Budweiser Champion Clydesdales is the first stein in Anheuser-Busch's long-running Holiday series. The relief design shows an eight-horse hitch traveling over a grassy green path. The rich browns of the horses are further accentuated by the antique brown background and complemented by the red accent line at rim. This stein was also issued in 1981 for a Tampa, Florida promotion.

Holiday Series

SIDE VIEW

DETAIL

Budweiser Champion Clydesdales

ISSUE YEAR:
1981
EDITION QUANTITY:
Open
ITEM NUMBER:
CS19A

T his early offering from Anheuser-Busch features the World Famous Budweiser Champion Clydesdales. Detailed in full relief, this half-liter presents the Clydesdale hitch along with an A&Eagle logo.

HEIGHT:
5″
ORIGIN:
Brazil
MANUFACTURER:
Ceramarte
MATERIAL:
Ceramic

Holiday Series

SIDE VIEW

DETAIL

Snowy Woodland

ISSUE YEAR:
1981

EDITION QUANTITY:
Open

ITEM NUMBER:
CS50

SERIES ORDER:
Second

HEIGHT:
6¼″

ORIGIN:
Brazil

MANUFACTURER:
Ceramarte

MATERIAL:
Ceramic

This barrel-shaped stein is the second in the Anheuser-Busch Holiday stein series. Illustrated in rich brown tones, the relief stein shows the eight-horse hitch traveling through a forest of snow-covered trees. A dotted pattern accents the border at the top, base and handle. The Budweiser logo featured in red lettering completes the stein.

Holiday Series

SIDE VIEW

DETAIL

50th Anniversary Celebration

ISSUE YEAR:
1982
EDITION QUANTITY:
Open
ITEM NUMBER:
CS57
SERIES ORDER:
Third

This stein celebrates the 50th anniversary of the World Famous Anheuser-Busch Clydesdales. The holiday design shows the eight-horse hitch proceeding along a snowy path past a log cabin. Accents include forest green borders top and bottom featuring "Clydesdales 50th Anniversary" and "1933-1983" in white lettering. "Budweiser" is shown in red lettering at the base.

HEIGHT:
6¼"
ORIGIN:
Brazil
MANUFACTURER:
Ceramarte
MATERIAL:
Ceramic

SIDE VIEW

DETAIL

ISSUE YEAR:
1983
EDITION QUANTITY:
Open
ITEM NUMBER:
CS58
SERIES ORDER:
Fourth

Cameo Wheatland

HEIGHT:
6½″
ORIGIN:
Brazil
MANUFACTURER:
Ceramarte
MATERIAL:
Ceramic
SPECIAL FEATURE:
Bottom Stamp

As the fourth addition in the Anheuser-Busch Holiday stein series, the Cameo Wheatland barrel-shaped design highlights the beautiful Clydesdales with two colorful images of the eight-horse hitch shown inside white cameo frames. The A&Eagle logo is centered against a barley and hops design.

Holiday Series

SIDE VIEW

DETAIL

Covered Bridge

ISSUE YEAR:
1984
EDITION QUANTITY:
Open
ITEM NUMBER:
CS62
SERIES ORDER:
Fifth

The 1984 Holiday Series stein showcases the Anheuser-Busch Clydesdales as they cross a covered bridge. Traveling through the snow, the eight-horse hitch passes through a tranquil evergreen forest. The design also includes a dotted green accent pattern at top and two red accents bands at base with Budweiser lettering in red.

HEIGHT:
6¼"
ORIGIN:
Brazil
MANUFACTURER:
Ceramarte
MATERIAL:
Ceramic
SPECIAL FEATURE:
Bottom Stamp

SIDE VIEW

DETAIL

ISSUE YEAR:
1985
EDITION QUANTITY:
Open
ITEM NUMBER:
CS63
SERIES ORDER:
Sixth

Snow Capped Mountains

HEIGHT:
6¼"
ORIGIN:
Brazil
MANUFACTURER:
Ceramarte
MATERIAL:
Ceramic
SPECIAL FEATURE:
Bottom Stamp

This relief conical stein is the sixth in the Anheuser-Busch Holiday series. The illustration shows an eight-horse hitch journeying through a breathtaking mountain pass. This scene is framed by a Budweiser banner quilted pattern design which complements the red bands and white roping accents. An A&Eagle logo appears on the thumbrest.

Holiday Series

SIDE VIEW

DETAIL

Traditional Houses

ISSUE YEAR:
1986
EDITION QUANTITY:
Open
ITEM NUMBER:
CS66
SERIES ORDER:
Seventh

Nineteenth century houses and the impressive Clydesdales eight-horse hitch are featured on the seventh stein of the Anheuser-Busch Holiday series. This conical-shaped stein has a red and white border designed to resemble the tassels worn by the hitch. A flowing red ribbon displays the Budweiser logo and sits on top of an A&Eagle emblem.

HEIGHT:
6¼"
ORIGIN:
Brazil
MANUFACTURER:
Ceramarte
MATERIAL:
Ceramic
SPECIAL FEATURES:
Certificate of Authenticity
Bottom Stamp
Gift Box

Holiday Series

SIDE VIEW

DETAIL

ISSUE YEAR:
1987
EDITION QUANTITY:
Open
ITEM NUMBER:
CS70
SERIES ORDER:
Eighth

Grant's Farm Gates

HEIGHT:
6½″
ORIGIN:
Brazil
MANUFACTURER:
Ceramarte
MATERIAL:
Ceramic
SPECIAL FEATURE:
Bottom Stamp

This detailed relief stein features the renowned Anheuser-Busch Clydesdales against a unique backdrop: the impressive Grant's Farm entry gates. A scalloped accent design traces the top and the handle of the stein. The words "Collector's Series, 1987" and an A&Eagle logo are also featured.

Holiday Series

Budweiser

SIDE VIEW

DETAIL

Cobblestone Passage

ISSUE YEAR:
1988
EDITION QUANTITY:
Open
ITEM NUMBER:
CS88
SERIES ORDER:
Ninth

The ninth addition to the long running Holiday series portrays the Clydesdales on a winter's journey. The eight-horse hitch follows a path along a grey stone bridge with a forest of trees in the background. The bottom of the stein features an attractive blue border with shiny holiday bells. The handle is detailed with a complementary white border.

HEIGHT:
6½″
ORIGIN:
Brazil
MANUFACTURER:
Ceramarte
MATERIAL:
Ceramic
SPECIAL FEATURE:
Bottom Stamp

Holiday Series

SIDE VIEW

DETAIL

ISSUE YEAR:
1989
EDITION QUANTITY:
Open
ITEM NUMBER:
CS89
SERIES ORDER:
Tenth

Winter Evening

HEIGHT:
6½"
ORIGIN:
Brazil
MANUFACTURER:
Ceramarte
MATERIAL:
Ceramic
SPECIAL FEATURE:
Bottom Stamp

The tenth stein in the Anheuser-Busch Holiday series features an attractive illustration of the Clydesdales eight-horse hitch on a snowy winter evening. The horses are traveling past snow-covered roofs highlighted by a deep blue sky. The design also includes the trademark A&Eagle symbol which interrupts a rich gold and brown border.

Holiday Series

SIDE VIEW

DETAIL

An American Tradition

ISSUE YEAR:
1990
EDITION QUANTITY:
CS112: Open
CS112SE: 10,000
CS112GOLD: 1,500
ITEM NUMBER:
CS112, CS112SE &
*CS112GOLD**
SERIES ORDER:
Eleventh

An American Tradition is the eleventh stein in the popular Holiday stein series and the first of three by artist Susan Sampson. This artist beautifully captures the spirit of the holidays as the Clydesdales eight-horse hitch passes a snowy-banked pond. This attractive scene is framed by red and blue accents and trimmed in gold.

HEIGHT:
7"
ORIGIN:
Brazil
MANUFACTURER:
Ceramarte
MATERIAL:
Ceramic
SPECIAL FEATURES:
Certificate of Authenticity
Bottom Stamp
CS112SE: Artist Signature
CS112GOLD: Gold Decal
ARTIST:
Susan Renae Sampson

*CS112SE Signature Edition; CS112GOLD Wholesaler Gold Decal Edition

Holiday Series

SIDE VIEW

DETAIL

ISSUE YEAR:
1991
EDITION QUANTITY:
CS133: Open
CS133SE: 10,000
CS133GOLD: 1,500
ITEM NUMBER:
CS133, CS133SE &
CS133GOLD*
SERIES ORDER:
Twelfth

HEIGHT:
7″
ORIGIN:
Brazil
MANUFACTURER:
Ceramarte
MATERIAL:
Ceramic
SPECIAL FEATURES:
Bottom Stamp
CS133SE: Artist Signature
CS133GOLD: Gold Decal
ARTIST:
Susan Renae Sampson

The Season's Best

Susan Sampson's The Season's Best is a nostalgic look at the majestic Clydesdales eight-horse hitch as the team of horses pauses at a quiet tree farm on a cold winter's day. The twelfth addition to the series features an engaging illustration filled with color and subtleties, making it a worthy member of this attractive series of holiday steins.

*CS133SE *Signature Edition;* CS133GOLD *Wholesaler Gold Decal Edition*

Holiday Series

SIDE VIEW

DETAIL

A Perfect Christmas

ISSUE YEAR:
1992
EDITION QUANTITY:
CS167: Open
CS167SE: 10,000
CS167GOLD: 1,500
ITEM NUMBER:
CS167, CS167SE &
CS167GOLD*
SERIES ORDER:
Thirteenth

The thirteenth in Anheuser-Busch's ongoing Holiday series, A Perfect Christmas depicts the Clydesdales hitch traveling through a small town on a cold winter's day. In her third and final work, artist Susan Sampson has designed a festive scene with striking colors. The stein's rims and handle have black and red bands with gold accent rims.

HEIGHT:
7"
ORIGIN:
Brazil
MANUFACTURER:
Ceramarte
MATERIAL:
Ceramic
SPECIAL FEATURES:
Bottom Stamp
CS167SE: Artist Signature
CS167GOLD: Gold Decal
ARTIST:
Susan Renae Sampson

*CS167SE Signature Edition; CS167GOLD Wholesaler Gold Decal Edition

Holiday Series

SIDE VIEW

DETAIL

ISSUE YEAR:
1993
EDITION QUANTITY:
CS192: Open
CS192SE: 10,000
CS192GOLD: 1,500
ITEM NUMBER:
CS192, CS192SE &
CS192GOLD*
SERIES ORDER:
Fourteenth

HEIGHT:
6¾″
ORIGIN:
Brazil
MANUFACTURER:
Ceramarte
MATERIAL:
Ceramic
SPECIAL FEATURES:
Certificate of Authenticity
Bottom Stamp
Gift Box
CS192SE: Artist Signature
CS192GOLD: Gold Decal
ARTIST:
Nora Koerber

Special Delivery

Lidded (Signature Edition Only)

Special Delivery is the fourteenth stein in the ongoing Holiday series. Artist Nora Koerber has illustrated a winter scene depicting the World Famous Clydesdales traveling over a snowy path against a beautiful mountain backdrop. The green bands at top and bottom are accented with pine cones and Budweiser red lettering.

*CS192SE Signature Edition; CS192GOLD Wholesaler Gold Decal Edition

Holiday Series

SIDE VIEW

DETAIL

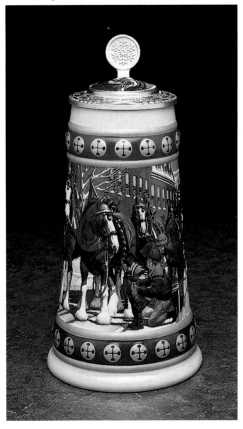

Hometown Holiday

Lidded (Signature Edition Only)

ISSUE YEAR:
1994

EDITION QUANTITY:
CS211: Open
CS211SE: 10,000
CS211GOLD: 1,500

ITEM NUMBER:
CS211, CS211SE &
CS211GOLD

SERIES ORDER:
Fifteenth

Longtime Anheuser-Busch stein artist Bud Kemper provides the inspiration for the 15th edition in the Holiday Stein Series. The detailed illustration features a delighted American family admiring the Budweiser Clydesdale hitch, which has come to town for Christmas. The lidded edition's pewter lid has a Clydesdale ceramic inlay.

HEIGHT:
7½"

ORIGIN:
Brazil

MANUFACTURER:
Ceramarte

SPECIAL FEATURES:
Certificate of Authenticity
Bottom Stamp
Gift Box
CS211SE: Artist Signature
CS211GOLD: Gold Decal

ARTIST:
Bud Kemper

*CS211SE Signature Edition; CS211GOLD Wholesaler Gold Decal Edition

Holiday Series

SIDE VIEW

DETAIL

ISSUE YEAR:
1995

EDITION QUANTITY:
CS263: Open
CS263SE: 10,000
CS263GOLD: 1,500

ITEM NUMBER:
CS263, CS263SE &
CS263GOLD

SERIES ORDER:
Sixteenth

HEIGHT:
7½"

ORIGIN:
Brazil

MANUFACTURER:
Ceramarte

SPECIAL FEATURES:
Certificate of Authenticity
Bottom Stamp
Gift Box
CS263SE: Artist Signature
CS263GOLD: Gold Decal

ARTIST:
Tom Jester

Lighting the Way Home

Lidded (Signature Edition Only)

This 16th stein in the Holiday Series depicts the world-famous Budweiser Clydesdale eight-horse hitch dashing past a nostalgic lighthouse in a winter seaside scene. Bands of snowflakes at top and bottom add a unique touch. The lidded Signature Edition features a detailed pewter lid with a colorful Clydesdale ceramic inlay.

*CS263SE Signature Edition; CS263GOLD Wholesaler Gold Decal Edition

Clydesdales Steins

August A. Busch, Jr. gave the first Clydesdales hitch to his father in 1933. Since that time, the eight-horse hitch has become a beloved symbol of Anheuser-Busch Inc., performing for delighted audiences across the United States. Decorated with lush color and beautiful detail, these majestic horses are brought to life in this distinctive group of fine steins. ❧

Clydesdales Steins

Contents of This Section

SIDE VIEW

DETAIL

ISSUE YEAR:
1976
EDITION QUANTITY:
Open
ITEM NUMBER:
CSL9

Clydesdales

Lidded

HEIGHT:
5¾"
ORIGIN:
Brazil
MANUFACTURER:
Ceramarte
MATERIAL:
Ceramic
LID:
Pewter

The Anheuser-Busch World Famous Clydesdales are illustrated on this unique full relief stein. The eight-horse hitch is circling the ceramic stein. In addition, the stein has a distinctive pounded pewter flat lid and rounded thumbrest. This is the lidded version of CS19A.

SIDE VIEW

DETAIL

Clydesdales

ISSUE YEAR:
1976
EDITION QUANTITY:
Open
ITEM NUMBER:
CS15

This relief stein shows a winter view of the famous Budweiser Clydesdales eight-horse hitch. Here the team is depicted at the entrance to Grant's Farm, an historic St. Louis landmark. The horses are traveling a dirt path through towering trees and green grass. The Anheuser-Busch A&Eagle is featured in red.

HEIGHT:
6″
ORIGIN:
Brazil
MANUFACTURER:
Ceramarte
MATERIAL:
Ceramic
SPECIAL FEATURE:
Certificate of Authenticity

SIDE VIEW

DETAIL

ISSUE YEAR:
1976
EDITION QUANTITY:
Open
ITEM NUMBER:
CSL29

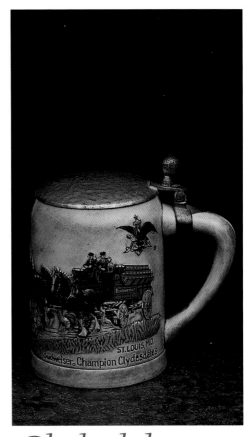

Clydesdales

Lidded

HEIGHT:
5½″
ORIGIN:
Brazil
MANUFACTURER:
Ceramarte
MATERIAL:
Ceramic
LID:
Pewter

The Anheuser-Busch World Famous Budweiser Clydesdales are illustrated on this unique full relief stein, traveling around the body. An added feature is the distinctive pounded-pewter flat lid and rounded thumbrest.

SIDE VIEW

DETAIL

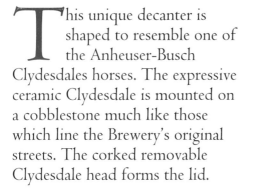

Clydesdale Decanter

Lidded

ISSUE YEAR:
1976
EDITION QUANTITY:
Open
ITEM NUMBER:
CS33

This unique decanter is shaped to resemble one of the Anheuser-Busch Clydesdales horses. The expressive ceramic Clydesdale is mounted on a cobblestone much like those which line the Brewery's original streets. The corked removable Clydesdale head forms the lid.

HEIGHT:
9″H x 8¼″W x 5¼″D
ORIGIN:
Brazil
MANUFACTURER:
Ceramarte
MATERIAL:
Ceramic
LID:
Ceramic

SIDE VIEW

DETAIL

ISSUE YEAR:
1983
EDITION QUANTITY:
Open
ITEM NUMBER:
CS61

Bud Light Baron

HEIGHT:
6½″
ORIGIN:
Brazil
MANUFACTURER:
Ceramarte
MATERIAL:
Ceramic

This relief stein salutes the Anheuser-Busch Clydesdale featured in the introduction of Bud Light beer. "Baron" is featured on both sides of the stein with the A&Eagle symbol framed in a horseshoe made of grain. The original Bud Light logo is also included on the stein.

SIDE VIEW

DETAIL

Horseshoe

ISSUE YEAR:
1986

Open
ITEM NUMBER:
CS68

The Budweiser Horseshoe stein is distinguished by an unusual platinum finished horseshoe, depicting the World Famous Budweiser Clydesdales eight-horse hitch. Hand-crafted styling and a detailed A&Eagle logo accentuate the stein. An exact duplicate to stein cs77, this version was produced in West Germany.

HEIGHT:
6¾"
ORIGIN:
West Germany
MANUFACTURER:
Gerz
MATERIAL:
Ceramic
SPECIAL FEATURE:
Bottom Stamp

SIDE VIEW

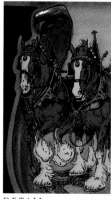

DETAIL

ISSUE YEAR:
1987
EDITION QUANTITY:
Open
ITEM NUMBER:
CS77

Horseshoe

HEIGHT:
6¾″
ORIGIN:
Brazil
MANUFACTURER:
Ceramarte
MATERIAL:
Ceramic
SPECIAL FEATURE:
Bottom Stamp

The Budweiser Horseshoe ceramic stein is distinguished by an unusual platinum finished horseshoe, depicting the World Famous Budweiser Clydesdales eight-horse hitch. The handcrafted styling and detailed A&Eagle logo also accent the stein.

SIDE VIEW

DETAIL

Horsehead

ISSUE YEAR:
1987
EDITION QUANTITY:
Open
ITEM NUMBER:
CS78

This decorative stein pays tribute to the World Famous Budweiser Clydesdales. A portrait of two of these horses is framed in an oval on both sides of the stein. The A&Eagle corporate symbol is framed by a barley and hops design. A duplicate to stein CS76, this version was produced in West Germany.

HEIGHT:
6¾"
ORIGIN:
West Germany
MANUFACTURER:
Gerz
MATERIAL:
Ceramic
SPECIAL FEATURE:
Bottom Stamp

SIDE VIEW

DETAIL

ISSUE YEAR:
1987
EDITION QUANTITY:
Open
ITEM NUMBER:
CS76

Horsehead

HEIGHT:
6¾"
ORIGIN:
Brazil
MANUFACTURER:
Ceramarte
MATERIAL:
Ceramic

This decorative stein pays tribute to the World Famous Budweiser Clydesdales. A portrait of two of these horses is framed in an oval on both sides of the stein. The A&Eagle corporate symbol is framed by a barley and hops design.

SIDE VIEW

DETAIL

Horse Harness

ISSUE YEAR:
1988
EDITION QUANTITY:
Open
ITEM NUMBER:
CS94

This 1988 stein, the third in the memorable Horseshoe Series, showcases all the drama and pageantry of the Budweiser Clydesdales in full parade dress and harness. Detailed in intricate relief, the artwork creates an original snapshot of the beautiful eight-horse hitch.

HEIGHT:
6¾"
ORIGIN:
Brazil
MANUFACTURER:
Ceramarte
MATERIAL:
Ceramic
SPECIAL FEATURE:
Bottom Stamp

SIDE VIEW

DETAIL

ISSUE YEAR:
1987
EDITION QUANTITY:
Open
ITEM NUMBER:
CS74
SERIES ORDER:
First

World Famous Clydesdales

HEIGHT:
5½″
ORIGIN:
Brazil
MANUFACTURER:
Ceramarte
MATERIAL:
Ceramic
SPECIAL FEATURE:
Bottom Stamp

The Budweiser Clydesdales, a true world famous team of horses, is featured on this original ceramic stein. Detailed in full relief, the richly colored antique wash provides a complementary backdrop for the eight-horse hitch. The A&Eagle trademark is also depicted in full relief near the handle.

Clydesdales Series

SIDE VIEW

DETAIL

Mare & Foal

ISSUE YEAR:
1988
EDITION QUANTITY:
Open
ITEM NUMBER:
CS90
SERIES ORDER:
Second

The second edition in the Clydesdales Collection shows a heart-warming depiction of a Clydesdale mare with her young foal. The new mother is gracefully running with the foal in a serene, natural setting. This detailed relief stein also features the A&Eagle trademark near the handle.

HEIGHT:
5½"
ORIGIN:
Brazil
MANUFACTURER:
Ceramarte
MATERIAL:
Ceramic
SPECIAL FEATURE:
Bottom Stamp

SIDE VIEW

DETAIL

ISSUE YEAR:
1989
EDITION QUANTITY:
Open
ITEM NUMBER:
CS99
SERIES ORDER:
Third

HEIGHT:
5½"
ORIGIN:
Brazil
MANUFACTURER:
Ceramarte
MATERIAL:
Ceramic
SPECIAL FEATURE:
Bottom Stamp

Parade Dress

The ceramic Parade Dress stein is the third in the Clydesdales series. This view of the Budweiser Clydesdales shows the ornate Parade Dress which can be seen at a number of the teams' official appearances. The A&Eagle trademark is featured in relief near the handle.

Clydesdales Series

SIDE VIEW

DETAIL

Clydesdales Training Hitch

ISSUE YEAR:
1991
EDITION QUANTITY:
Open
ITEM NUMBER:
CS131
SERIES ORDER:
Fourth

The Clydesdales Training Hitch edition depicts a Clydesdale preparing to become a member of the World Famous team. The horse, practicing on this special hitch, is detailed in rich tones and full relief. The artwork created for this handcrafted ceramic stein is steeped in the time-honored tradition of these famous horses.

HEIGHT:
5½"
ORIGIN:
Brazil
MANUFACTURER:
Ceramarte
MATERIAL:
Ceramic
SPECIAL FEATURE:
Bottom Stamp

SIDE VIEW

DETAIL

ISSUE YEAR:
1992
EDITION QUANTITY:
Open
ITEM NUMBER:
CS161
SERIES ORDER:
Fifth

Clydesdales On Parade

HEIGHT:
5½"
ORIGIN:
Brazil
MANUFACTURER:
Ceramarte
MATERIAL:
Ceramic
SPECIAL FEATURES:
Bottom Stamp
Gift Box

The Clydesdales On Parade stein is the fifth edition to the Clydesdales series. The World Famous ambassadors of Budweiser are making their way across the attractive ceramic stein detailed in full relief. The A&Eagle trademark and the title "World Famous Budweiser Clydesdales" are featured in relief near the handle.

SIDE VIEW

DETAIL

Proud
and Free

ISSUE YEAR:
1994
EDITION QUANTITY:
Open
ITEM NUMBER:
CS223

The world-famous ambassadors of Budweiser, the Clydesdales, are featured on this 5½" tall ceramic relief stein. A beautifully detailed illustration circles the stein, showing the powerful and graceful Clydesdales running proud and free.

HEIGHT:
5½"
ORIGIN:
Brazil
MANUFACTURER:
Ceramarte
MATERIAL:
Ceramic
SPECIAL FEATURE:
Certificate of Authenticity
Bottom Stamp
Gift Box

Notes

Brewery Specific Steins

A nheuser-Busch's century-old commitment to quality, which began with Adolphus Busch, remains the brewery's driving force to this day. No matter what the subject matter, from the history of the brewing process to the historical landmarks on the Anheuser-Busch properties, each of these steins symbolizes that same, unwavering commitment to quality products. ∽

Brewery Specific Steins

Contents of This Section

SIDE VIEW

DETAIL

ISSUE YEAR:
Not Available
EDITION QUANTITY:
Not Available
ITEM NUMBER:
Not Available

Adolphus Busch

Lidded

HEIGHT:
9″
ORIGIN:
Germany
MANUFACTURER:
Villeroy & Boch
MATERIAL:
Ceramic
LID:
Pewter with Ceramic Inlay
SPECIAL FEATURES:
Handpainted Bottom Stamp

This striking stein depicts Adolphus Busch, founder and original president of the Anheuser-Busch Brewery. The beautifully colored stein is topped with a pewter lid featuring the A&Eagle symbol in ceramic inlay and includes an eagle-shaped thumbrest. Adolphus Busch was highly skilled in advertising and promoting his products. This stein pays tribute to his expertise.

History of Brewing Series

SIDE VIEW

DETAIL

Limited Edition I

Lidded

ISSUE YEAR:
1985
EDITION QUANTITY:
200,000
ITEM NUMBER:
CS64
SERIES ORDER:
First

The Limited Edition I stein is the first in the vintage History of Brewing series. This version, antiqued and decorated with ornate trim, features an A&Eagle trademark at center. A decorative ribbon with the words "Anheuser-Busch, Inc." and "King of Beers" wraps around the body. Brewing and fermentation scenes are illustrated and framed by oval relief designs on both sides of the stein.

HEIGHT:
9½″
ORIGIN:
Brazil
MANUFACTURER:
Ceramarte
MATERIAL:
Ceramic
LID:
Pewter
SPECIAL FEATURES:
Individually Numbered
Certificate of Authenticity
Bottom Stamp
Gift Box

SIDE VIEW

DETAIL

ISSUE YEAR:
1986
EDITION QUANTITY:
200,000
ITEM NUMBER:
CS65
SERIES ORDER:
Second

HEIGHT:
9½"
ORIGIN:
Brazil
MANUFACTURER:
Ceramarte
MATERIAL:
Ceramic
LID:
Pewter
SPECIAL FEATURES:
Individually Numbered
Certificate of Authenticity
Bottom Stamp
Gift Box

Limited Edition II

Lidded

The Limited Edition II stein is the second in the vintage History of Brewing series. This version, antiqued and decorated with ornate trim, features an A&Eagle trademark at center. A decorative ribbon with the words "Anheuser-Busch, Inc." and "King of Beers" wraps around the body. Aging and cooperage scenes are illustrated and framed by oval relief designs on both sides of the stein.

History of Brewing Series

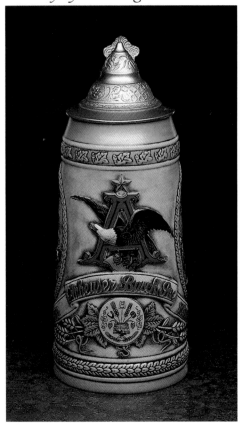

SIDE VIEW

DETAIL

Limited Edition III

Lidded

ISSUE YEAR:
1987
EDITION QUANTITY:
200,000
ITEM NUMBER:
CS71
SERIES ORDER:
Third

The Limited Edition III stein is the third in the vintage History of Brewing series. Antiqued with ornate trim, it features an A&Eagle trademark at center. Scenes of a clipper ship and a horse-drawn wagon are illustrated and framed by oval relief designs on both sides of the stein.

HEIGHT:
9½"
ORIGIN:
Brazil
MANUFACTURER:
Ceramarte
MATERIAL:
Ceramic
LID:
Pewter
SPECIAL FEATURES:
Individually Numbered
Certificate of Authenticity
Bottom Stamp
Gift Box

SIDE VIEW

DETAIL

ISSUE YEAR:
1988
EDITION QUANTITY:
200,000
ITEM NUMBER:
CS75
SERIES ORDER:
Fourth

Limited Edition IV

Lidded

HEIGHT:
9½"
ORIGIN:
Brazil
MANUFACTURER:
Ceramarte
MATERIAL:
Ceramic
LID:
Pewter
SPECIAL FEATURES:
Individually Numbered
Certificate of Authenticity
Bottom Stamp
Gift Box

The Limited Edition IV stein is the fourth in the vintage History of Brewing series. Antiqued and decorated with ornate trim, it features an A&Eagle trademark at center. A decorative ribbon with the words "Anheuser-Busch, Inc." and "King of Beers" wraps around the body. Traditional tavern and public house scenes are illustrated and framed by oval relief designs.

History of Brewing Series

SIDE VIEW

DETAIL

Limited Edition V

Lidded

ISSUE YEAR:
1989
EDITION QUANTITY:
200,000
ITEM NUMBER:
CS98
SERIES ORDER:
Fifth & Final

The Limited Edition V stein is the final in the vintage History of Brewing series. This version, antiqued and decorated with ornate trim, features an A&Eagle trademark at center. A decorative ribbon with the words "Anheuser-Busch, Inc." and "King of Beers" wraps around the body. Bavarian Festival scenes are illustrated and framed by oval relief designs on both sides of the stein.

HEIGHT:
9½"
ORIGIN:
Brazil
MANUFACTURER:
Ceramarte
MATERIAL:
Ceramic
LID:
Pewter
SPECIAL FEATURES:
Individually Numbered
Certificate of Authenticity
Bottom Stamp
Gift Box

SIDE VIEW

DETAIL

ISSUE YEAR:
1986
EDITION QUANTITY:
Open
ITEM NUMBER:
CS67
SERIES ORDER:
First

Brew House

HEIGHT:
7½"
ORIGIN:
Brazil
MANUFACTURER:
Ceramarte
MATERIAL:
Ceramic
SPECIAL FEATURES:
Certificate of Authenticity
Bottom Stamp
Gift Box
ARTIST:
Don Langeneckert

The Brew House is the introductory stein in the Historical Landmark series. Accented with A&Eagle symbols circling the top, the relief stein showcases both the Anheuser-Busch Brew House and the World Famous Budweiser Clydesdales. The Anheuser-Busch Brew House, in use since 1892, is a national historic landmark.

Historical Landmark Series

SIDE VIEW

DETAIL

Budweiser Stables

ISSUE YEAR:
1987
EDITION QUANTITY:
Open
ITEM NUMBER:
CS73
SERIES ORDER:
Second

The Budweiser Clydesdales Stables are beautifully depicted on the second stein in the Historical Landmark series. Erected in 1885, the vintage stables are vividly illustrated to showcase the original stained-glass windows and ornate lighting fixtures.

HEIGHT:
7½"
ORIGIN:
Brazil
MANUFACTURER:
Ceramarte
MATERIAL:
Ceramic
SPECIAL FEATURES:
Individually Numbered
Certificate of Authenticity
Bottom Stamp
Gift Box
ARTIST:
Don Langeneckert

SIDE VIEW

DETAIL

ISSUE YEAR:
1988
EDITION QUANTITY:
Open
ITEM NUMBER:
CS83
SERIES ORDER:
Third

Grant's Cabin

HEIGHT:
7½"
ORIGIN:
Brazil
MANUFACTURER:
Ceramarte
MATERIAL:
Ceramic
SPECIAL FEATURES:
Individually Numbered
Certificate of Authenticity
Bottom Stamp
Gift Box
ARTIST:
Don Langeneckert

The third edition in the Historical Landmark series, Grant's Cabin, shows the boyhood home of President Ulysses S. Grant. Located on Grant's Farm natural game preserve, the 1854 cabin is attractively depicted here in full relief.

Historical Landmark Series

SIDE VIEW

DETAIL

Old School House

ISSUE YEAR:
1988
EDITION QUANTITY:
Open
ITEM NUMBER:
CS84
SERIES ORDER:
Fourth & Final

Old School House is the fourth and final stein in the Historical Landmark series. The relief design remembers the historic building, still a part of the Anheuser-Busch complex. The Old School House is a national historic landmark.

HEIGHT:
7½″
ORIGIN:
Brazil
MANUFACTURER:
Ceramarte
MATERIAL:
Ceramic
SPECIAL FEATURES:
Certificate of Authenticity
Bottom Stamp
Gift Box
ARTIST:
Don Langeneckert

SIDE VIEW

DETAIL

ISSUE YEAR:
1988

EDITION QUANTITY:
20,000

ITEM NUMBER:
CS93

SERIES ORDER:
First

Classic I

Lidded

HEIGHT:
8¼″

ORIGIN:
Germany

MANUFACTURER:
Gerz

MATERIAL:
Ceramic

LID:
Pewter with Ceramic Inlay

SPECIAL FEATURES:
*Individually Numbered
Certificate of Authenticity
Bottom Stamp
Gift Box*

ARTIST:
Don Langeneckert

The Classic I stein depicts the Anheuser-Busch Brewery in the 1890s. Illustrated from archive lithographs, the panoramic scene showcases the period architecture. The antique look is enhanced with century-old lettering and the A&Eagle symbol. An attractive ceramic inlaid pewter lid tops the stein.

Classic Series

SIDE VIEW

DETAIL

Classic II

ISSUE YEAR:
1989
EDITION QUANTITY:
20,000
ITEM NUMBER:
CS104
SERIES ORDER:
Second

Lidded

The Classic II stein depicts the Anheuser-Busch Brew House as it looked in the 1890s. Illustrated from archive lithographs, the beautiful decor includes numerous columns, a detailed banister and a stunning chandelier. The antique look is enhanced with century-old lettering and the A&Eagle symbol. An attractive ceramic inlaid pewter lid tops the stein.

HEIGHT:
8¼″
ORIGIN:
Germany
MANUFACTURER:
Gerz
MATERIAL:
Ceramic
LID:
Pewter with Ceramic Inlay
SPECIAL FEATURES:
*Individually Numbered
Certificate of Authenticity
Bottom Stamp
Gift Box*
ARTIST:
Don Langeneckert

SIDE VIEW

DETAIL

ISSUE YEAR:
1990
EDITION QUANTITY:
20,000
ITEM NUMBER:
CS113
SERIES ORDER:
Third

Classic III

Lidded

HEIGHT:
8¼″
ORIGIN:
Germany
MANUFACTURER:
Gerz
MATERIAL:
Ceramic
LID:
Pewter with Ceramic Inlay
SPECIAL FEATURES:
Individually Numbered Certificate of Authenticity Bottom Stamp Gift Box
ARTIST:
Don Langeneckert

The Classic III stein depicts the E. Anheuser & Co. Brewery as it looked at the turn of the century. The antique look is enhanced with century-old typography and the A&Eagle symbol. An attractive ceramic inlaid pewter lid tops the stein.

93

Classic Series

SIDE VIEW

DETAIL

Classic IV

ISSUE YEAR:
1991
EDITION QUANTITY:
25,000
ITEM NUMBER:
CS130
SERIES ORDER:
Fourth & Final

Lidded

This stein captures the bustling spirit of the St. Louis Levee in the late 1870s. The detailed relief features barrels of Anheuser-Busch beer ready to be loaded on Mississippi river boats. In the background is the Eads Bridge, the main thoroughfare spanning the Mississippi after 1874. An attractive ceramic inlaid pewter lid tops the stein.

HEIGHT:
8¼″
ORIGIN:
Germany
MANUFACTURER:
Gerz
MATERIAL:
Ceramic
LID:
Pewter with Ceramic Inlay
SPECIAL FEATURES:
*Individually Numbered
Certificate of Authenticity
Bottom Stamp
Gift Box*
ARTIST:
Don Langeneckert

SIDE VIEW

DETAIL

ISSUE YEAR:
1990
EDITION QUANTITY:
20,000
ITEM NUMBER:
CS105
SERIES ORDER:
First

Berninghaus

Lidded

HEIGHT:
9¾″
ORIGIN:
Germany
MANUFACTURER:
Rastal
MATERIAL:
Porcelain
LID:
Pewter
SPECIAL FEATURES:
Individually Numbered
Certificate of Authenticity
Bottom Stamp
Gift Box

This striking stein reprises artwork from the private collection of the Busch family. Renowned artist Oscar Berninghaus rendered this enchanting "Merry Christmas" design of Santa taking flight on a giant A&Eagle, the Anheuser-Busch trademark. The handcrafted porcelain stein is decorated with gold rim accents and an ornate solid pewter lid.

Porcelain Heritage Series

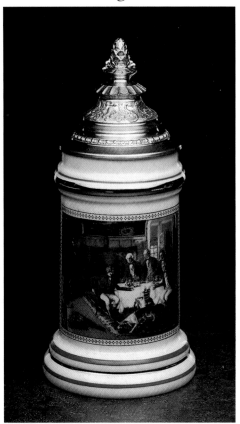

SIDE VIEW

DETAIL

After The Hunt

Lidded

ISSUE YEAR:
1991
EDITION QUANTITY:
25,000
ITEM NUMBER:
CS155
SERIES ORDER:
Second

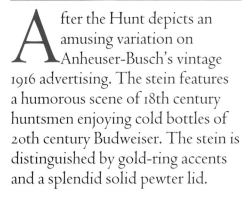

After the Hunt depicts an amusing variation on Anheuser-Busch's vintage 1916 advertising. The stein features a humorous scene of 18th century huntsmen enjoying cold bottles of 20th century Budweiser. The stein is distinguished by gold-ring accents and a splendid solid pewter lid.

HEIGHT:
9¾"
ORIGIN:
Germany
MANUFACTURER:
Rastal
MATERIAL:
Porcelain
LID:
Pewter
SPECIAL FEATURES:
Individually Numbered
Certificate of Authenticity
Bottom Stamp
Gift Box

Porcelain Heritage Series

SIDE VIEW

DETAIL

ISSUE YEAR:
1992
EDITION QUANTITY:
25,000
ITEM NUMBER:
CS182
SERIES ORDER:
Third

Cherub

Lidded

HEIGHT:
10¾″
ORIGIN:
Germany
MANUFACTURER:
Gerz
MATERIAL:
Porcelain
LID:
Pewter
SPECIAL FEATURES:
Individually Numbered
Certificate of Authenticity
Bottom Stamp
Gift Box
ARTIST:
Don Langeneckert

This stein beautifully showcases century-old Anheuser-Busch advertising art. The nostalgic scene shows a gathering of cherubs holding the brewer's turn-of-the-century beers: Budweiser, Black and Tan dark porter beer, Pale Lager and Malt Nutrine, a pharmaceutical product. A solid pewter relief lid completes the Cherub Stein, third in the Porcelain Heritage series.

Archives Series

SIDE VIEW

DETAIL

Columbian Exposition

Lidded

ISSUE YEAR:
1992
EDITION QUANTITY:
150,000
ITEM NUMBER:
CS169
SERIES ORDER:
First

The first in this handcrafted series of steins, this edition borrows from a painting in the Anheuser-Busch archives. The attractive illustration, depicting the U.S. toasting Christopher Columbus on the 400th anniversary of his historic voyage, was part of Anheuser-Busch's exhibit at the 1893 Columbian Exposition in Chicago. The detailed lid is pewter with a ceramic inlay.

HEIGHT:
7½"
ORIGIN:
Brazil
MANUFACTURER:
Ceramarte
MATERIAL:
Ceramic
LID:
Pewter with Ceramic Inlay
SPECIAL FEATURES:
*Individually Numbered
Certificate of Authenticity
Bottom Stamp
Gift Box*
ARTIST:
Don Langeneckert

SIDE VIEW

DETAIL

ISSUE YEAR:
1993
EDITION QUANTITY:
75,000
ITEM NUMBER:
CS190
SERIES ORDER:
Second

Ganymede

Lidded

HEIGHT:
6½"
ORIGIN:
Brazil
MANUFACTURER:
Ceramarte
MATERIAL:
Ceramic
LID:
*Pewter with
Ceramic Inlay*
SPECIAL FEATURES:
*Individually Numbered
Certificate of Authenticity
Bottom Stamp
Gift Box*
ARTIST:
Don Langeneckert

This stein depicts a popular turn-of-the-century advertising sign in which Ganymede is being carried aloft to Mt. Olympus, to serve Zeus. The eagle clasps a classic bottle of Budweiser, while Ganymede holds a decree stating Budweiser's superior quality. The pewter lid with ceramic inlay features an antique A&Eagle on the thumbrest.

Archives Series

SIDE VIEW

DETAIL

Budweiser's Greatest Triumph
Lidded

ISSUE YEAR:
1994
EDITION QUANTITY:
75,000
ITEM NUMBER:
CS222

This third edition in the series features dramatic turn-of-the-century advertising artwork, remarkably reproduced in full-color ceramic relief. The classic figure depicted in the illustration is symbolically proclaiming "Budweiser's Greatest Triumph." The stein's pewter lid includes a full-color ceramic relief inlay and an antique A&Eagle logo on the thumbrest.

HEIGHT:
6½″
ORIGIN:
Brazil
MANUFACTURER:
Ceramarte
MATERIAL:
Ceramic
LID:
Pewter with Ceramic Inlay
SPECIAL FEATURES:
Individually Numbered Certificate of Authenticity Bottom Stamp Gift Box
ARTIST:
Don Langeneckert

SIDE VIEW

DETAIL

ISSUE YEAR:
1995
EDITION QUANTITY:
75,000
ITEM NUMBER:
CS252

Mirror of Truth

Lidded

HEIGHT:
6½"
ORIGIN:
Brazil
MANUFACTURER:
Ceramarte
MATERIAL:
Ceramic
LID:
Pewter with Ceramic Inlay
SPECIAL FEATURES:
Individually Numbered Certificate of Authenticity Bottom Stamp Gift Box
ARTIST:
Don Langeneckert

Exceptional vintage artwork is once again showcased on this fourth and final stein in the Archives Series. The full-color illustration depicts a classic female figure shining a light from a symbolic "mirror of truth" onto a bottle of Budweiser, revealing its genuine quality and authentic flavor. The stein has a pewter lid with a ceramic inlay and an antique A&Eagle logo on the thumbrest.

A&Eagle Trademark Series

SIDE VIEW

DETAIL

A&Eagle Trademark I With Tin

ITEM NUMBER/
ISSUE YEAR:
CS201 Stein/Tin 1992
CS191 Stein/Box 1993
EDITION QUANTITY:
CS201: 30,000
CS191: 20,000
SERIES ORDER:
First

The first stein in the A&Eagle Trademark series of four remembers the famous Anheuser-Busch A&Eagle symbol dating from 1872-1885. The uniquely shaped stein, dramatically colored in black, has an antique design with richly colored trim and detailed relief. This edition was sold as a set and included a matching octagonal tin. Stein also sold individually as item number CS191.

HEIGHT:
4¾"
TIN DIMENSIONS:
5¾"H x 7¼"W x 5½"D
ORIGIN:
Brazil
MANUFACTURERS:
Ceramarte–Stein
S.A. Meister–Tin
MATERIAL:
Ceramic
SPECIAL FEATURES:
Individually Numbered
Certificate of Authenticity
Bottom Stamp
Gift Box
ARTIST:
Don Langeneckert

A&Eagle Trademark Series

DETAIL

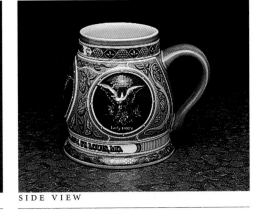

SIDE VIEW

ITEM NUMBER/
ISSUE YEAR:
CS218 Stein/Tin 1993
CS219 Stein/Box 1994
EDITION QUANTITY:
CS218: 20,000
CS219: 30,000
SERIES ORDER:
Second

A&Eagle Trademark II With Tin

HEIGHT:
4¾"
TIN DIMENSIONS:
5¾"H x 7¼"W x 5½"D
ORIGIN:
Brazil
MANUFACTURERS:
Ceramarte–Stein
S.A. Meister–Tin
MATERIAL:
Ceramic
SPECIAL FEATURES:
Individually Numbered
Certificate of Authenticity
Bottom Stamp
Gift Box
ARTIST:
Don Langeneckert

Second in the series of four, this stein continues the historical development of the A&Eagle logo. Featuring the logos of the 1890s, with the eagle's wings spread, this detailed relief stein marks the time period when Anheuser-Busch became America's leading brewery. The depictions of the A&Eagle logos are surrounded by intricate artwork of hops on the vine.

A&Eagle Trademark Series

SIDE VIEW

DETAIL

A&Eagle Trademark III With Tin

ITEM NUMBER/
ISSUE YEAR:
CS238 Stein/Tin 1994
CS240 Stein/Box 1995

EDITION QUANTITY:
CS238: 20,000
CS240: 30,000

SERIES ORDER:
Third

T his third edition in the historical series chronicles the evolution of the famous A&Eagle symbol over a period of almost 50 years. Three early versions of the logo are featured, including those used in the 1890s-1900s, 1910s and 1930s. The logos are displayed against black vignettes, between alternating panels of the Bevo Fox.

HEIGHT:
4¾"

TIN DIMENSIONS:
5¾"H x 7¼"W x 5½"D

ORIGIN:
Brazil

MANUFACTURERS:
Ceramarte–Stein
S.A. Meister–Tin

MATERIAL:
Ceramic

SPECIAL FEATURES:
Individually Numbered
Certificate of Authenticity
Bottom Stamp
Gift Box

ARTIST:
Don Langeneckert

A&Eagle Trademark Series

DETAIL

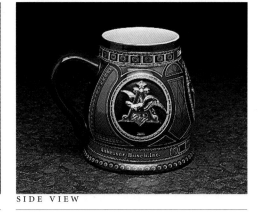

SIDE VIEW

ITEM NUMBER/
ISSUE YEAR:
CS255 Stein/Tin 1995
CS271 Stein/Box 1996
EDITION QUANTITY:
CS255: 20,000
CS271: 30,000
SERIES ORDER:
Fourth

HEIGHT:
4¾″
TIN DIMENSIONS:
5¾″H x 7¼″W x 5½″D
ORIGIN:
Brazil
MANUFACTURERS:
Ceramarte–Stein
S.A. Meister–Tin
MATERIAL:
Ceramic
SPECIAL FEATURES:
Individually Numbered
Certificate of Authenticity
Bottom Stamp
Gift Box
ARTIST:
Don Langeneckert

A&Eagle Trademark IV With Tin

A unique stein series comes to an end with this fourth and final edition in the historical A&Eagle Series. Three versions of the famous Anheuser-Busch A&Eagle logo are shown—those used during the 1930s, 1950s and 1970s. The design also features intricate patterns around the logos and detailed top and bottom bands.

Anheuser-Busch Founders Series

SIDE VIEW

DETAIL

Adolphus Busch

Lidded

ISSUE YEAR:
1993
EDITION QUANTITY:
10,000
ITEM NUMBER:
CS216
SERIES ORDER:
First

This intricate decorated and handpainted stein is a faithful reproduction of the original Adolphus Busch Mettlach stein produced by the renowned Villeroy & Boch. The unique lid, pewter with ceramic inlay, features the Anheuser-Busch A&Eagle company symbol. The detailed pewter thumbrest depicts an elaborate eagle design.

HEIGHT:
9"
ORIGIN:
Germany
MANUFACTURER:
Gerz
MATERIAL:
Ceramic
LID:
Pewter with Ceramic Inlay
SPECIAL FEATURES:
Individually Numbered
Certificate of Authenticity
Handpainted & Decaled
Bottom Stamp
Gift Box

Anheuser–Busch Founders Series

SIDE VIEW

DETAIL

ISSUE YEAR:
1994
EDITION QUANTITY:
10,000
ITEM NUMBER:
CS229
SERIES ORDER:
Second

August A. Busch, Sr.

Lidded

HEIGHT:
9″
ORIGIN:
Germany
MANUFACTURER:
Gerz
LID:
Pewter with Ceramic Inlay
SPECIAL FEATURES:
*Individually Numbered
Certificate of Authenticity
Bottom Stamp
Gift Box*

The second stein in the series salutes August A. Busch, Sr., Anheuser-Busch president from 1913 to 1934. His detailed portrait, the focal point of the stein, is flanked by many of the non-alcoholic products he developed to assure the company's survival during Prohibition. The pewter lid features an A&Eagle logo on a ceramic inlay and a detailed eagle as the thumbrest.

Anheuser-Busch Founders Series

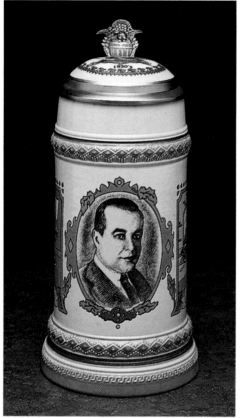

SIDE VIEW

DETAIL

Adolphus Busch III

Lidded

ISSUE YEAR:
1995

EDITION QUANTITY:
10,000

ITEM NUMBER:
CS265

SERIES ORDER:
Third

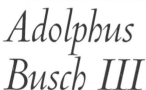

Adolphus Busch III is honored on this third stein in the series. In addition to a portrait of the Anheuser-Busch president from 1934 to 1946, the stein includes vintage artwork of the first can of Budweiser beer introduced in the 1930s—one of the many achievements made under his leadership. The pewter ceramic inlaid lid and detailed thumbrest are in keeping with the series.

HEIGHT:
9″

ORIGIN:
Germany

MANUFACTURER:
Gerz

LID:
Pewter with Ceramic Inlay

SPECIAL FEATURES:
Individually Numbered Certificate of Authenticity Bottom Stamp Gift Box

Notes

ABRAHAM LINCOLN

Specialty Steins

The steins in this section immortalize a variety of engaging themes. One popular character stein, Bud Man, is better known as Budweiser's dauntless defender of quality. Another character stein is the handpainted Bevo Fox, a favorite among collectors. In addition, the Specialty section includes steins which feature Anheuser-Busch's beer brands and illustrations which honor the winning spirit of the U.S. Olympic athletes. ～

Specialty Steins

Contents of This Section

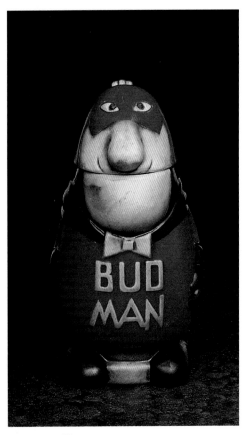

SIDE VIEW

DETAIL

Bud Man

1975 Style

Lidded

ISSUE YEAR:
1975
EDITION QUANTITY:
Open
ITEM NUMBER:
CS1

Anheuser-Busch's popular Bud Man is immortalized on this handcrafted character stein. His uniquely designed ceramic head forms the lid. Production of this stein included two versions of the lid, one solid and one hollow.

HEIGHT:
7½"
ORIGIN:
Brazil
MANUFACTURER:
Ceramarte
MATERIAL:
Ceramic

SIDE VIEW

DETAIL

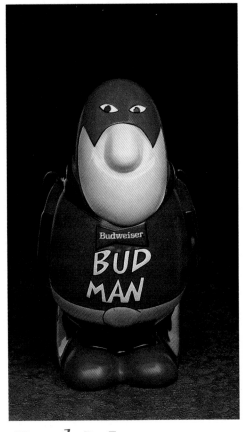

ISSUE YEAR:
1989
EDITION QUANTITY:
Open
ITEM NUMBER:
CS100

Bud Man

1989 Style

Lidded

HEIGHT:
8"
ORIGIN:
Brazil
MANUFACTURER:
Ceramarte
MATERIAL:
Ceramic
LID:
Ceramic
SPECIAL FEATURES:
Certificate of Authenticity
Gift Box

Vivid color and dimensional relief brings the Bud Man to life on this detailed ceramic stein. The dauntless defender of quality is depicted on this stylized stein, featuring Bud Man's head which forms the lid. A favorite of Bud fans and collectors alike.

SIDE VIEW

DETAIL

Bud Man

1993 Style

Lidded

ISSUE YEAR:
1993
EDITION QUANTITY:
Open
ITEM NUMBER:
CS213

This 1993 Bud Man character stein updates Anheuser-Busch's famous caped crusader of quality. The modern design shows a more slender Bud Man holding a can of ice cold Budweiser. The character's head lifts and is attached with a decorative pewter thumbrest.

HEIGHT:
8″
ORIGIN:
Brazil
MANUFACTURER:
Ceramarte
MATERIAL:
Ceramic
LID:
Ceramic
SPECIAL FEATURES:
Certificate of Authenticity
Bottom Stamp
Gift Box

SIDE VIEW

DETAIL

ISSUE YEAR:
1977
EDITION QUANTITY:
Open
ITEM NUMBER:
CS9

Natural Light

HEIGHT:
6"
ORIGIN:
Brazil
MANUFACTURER:
Ceramarte
MATERIAL:
Ceramic

Anheuser-Busch's first light beer trademark is remembered on this Natural Light half liter ceramic stein, complemented by the original red and blue Natural Light logo graphics.

SIDE VIEW

DETAIL

Budweiser Label

ISSUE YEAR:
1976
EDITION QUANTITY:
Open
ITEM NUMBER:
CS18

The famous Budweiser label graphics are highlighted on this boldly designed stein. Manufactured in full-relief, each side mirrors the traditional Budweiser can in bright red, white and blue.

HEIGHT:
5½″
ORIGIN:
Brazil
MANUFACTURER:
Ceramarte
MATERIAL:
Ceramic

SIDE VIEW

DETAIL

ISSUE YEAR:
1976
EDITION QUANTITY:
Open
ITEM NUMBER:
CS27

Michelob

HEIGHT:
5″
ORIGIN:
Brazil
MANUFACTURER:
Ceramarte
MATERIAL:
Ceramic

Deep black glazing creates a striking finish on this round-shaped Michelob stein. This dramatic half liter showcases the Michelob trademark graphics in gold decal. The Michelob inaugural date of 1896 is featured beneath the logo.

SIDE VIEW

DETAIL

King Cobra

ISSUE YEAR:
1987
EDITION QUANTITY:
Open
ITEM NUMBER:
CS80

The King Cobra logo is featured on this 5½″ stein and is distinguished with unique black, gold, red and white graphics.

HEIGHT:
5½″
ORIGIN:
Manufactured in USA
MATERIAL:
Ceramic

SIDE VIEW

DETAIL

Oktoberfest

ISSUE YEAR:
1980
EDITION QUANTITY:
Open
ITEM NUMBER:
CS42

Busch Gardens

HEIGHT:
5″
ORIGIN:
Brazil
MANUFACTURER:
Ceramarte
MATERIAL:
Ceramic

This gray, Bavarian-style Oktoberfest stein depicts The Old Country Theme Park in Williamsburg, Virginia.

Budweiser Oktoberfest Series

SIDE VIEW

DETAIL

Budweiser Oktoberfest

ISSUE YEAR:
1992
EDITION QUANTITY:
35,000
ITEM NUMBER:
CS185
SERIES ORDER:
Second

Budweiser celebrates the traditional Bavarian Oktoberfest with this detailed ceramic stein. The second in the Budweiser Oktoberfest series, this colorful stein depicts a crowded festival beer hall. Both the edges and handle are designed to resemble piping hot pretzels, a delicious German specialty at the Oktoberfest.

HEIGHT:
5½″
ORIGIN:
Brazil
MANUFACTURER:
Ceramarte
MATERIAL:
Ceramic
SPECIAL FEATURES:
Individually Numbered
Certificate of Authenticity
Bottom Stamp
Gift Box
ARTIST:
Marcy Wilson

Budweiser Oktoberfest Series

SIDE VIEW

DETAIL

ISSUE YEAR:
1993
EDITION QUANTITY:
35,000
ITEM NUMBER:
CS202
SERIES ORDER:
Third

1993 Budweiser Oktoberfest

HEIGHT:
5½"
ORIGIN:
Brazil
MANUFACTURER:
Ceramarte
MATERIAL:
Ceramic
SPECIAL FEATURES:
Individually Numbered
Certificate of Authenticity
Bottom Stamp
Gift Box

The final in the successful Budweiser Oktoberfest series, this stein celebrates both the rich heritage of this famous German celebration and the fine art of brewing. The relief design brings to life a horse-drawn beer wagon traveling through the quaint streets. Merry bands and dancing locals fill the stein's detailed background.

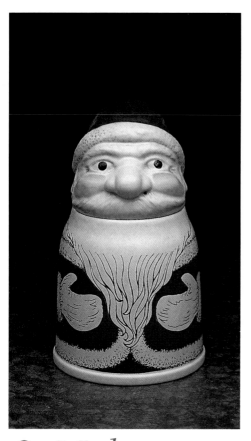

SIDE VIEW

DETAIL

St. Nick

ISSUE YEAR:
1987
EDITION QUANTITY:
Open
ITEM NUMBER:
CS79

Holiday Spirit is captured on this detailed character stein. St. Nick, crafted in ceramic, brings to life the traditional Santa Claus in festive reds and crisp white accents. St. Nick's head forms the lid and is attached to a pewter thumbrest.

HEIGHT:
7″
ORIGIN:
Germany
MANUFACTURER:
Gerz
MATERIAL:
Ceramic
LID:
Ceramic

SIDE VIEW

DETAIL

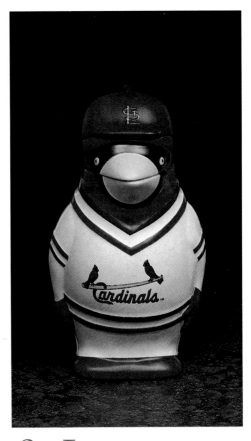

ISSUE YEAR:
1989
EDITION QUANTITY:
Open
ITEM NUMBER:
CS125

St. Louis Cardinals

Lidded

HEIGHT:
6½″
ORIGIN:
Brazil
MANUFACTURER:
Ceramarte
MATERIAL:
Ceramic
LID:
Ceramic
SPECIAL FEATURES:
Certificate of Authenticity
Gift Box

This character stein immortalizes a very important member of the St. Louis Cardinals' baseball team: the official team mascot. Wearing a team uniform and holding a baseball, the cardinal character is colored in striking red and white with blue and yellow accents. A pewter thumbrest opens the lid which is shaped like the cardinal's head.

SIDE VIEW

DETAIL

Bevo Fox

ISSUE YEAR:
1991
EDITION QUANTITY:
10,000
ITEM NUMBER:
CS160

Lidded

The Bevo Fox has been associated with Anheuser-Busch since 1916 when it was chosen to represent Bevo, a non-intoxicating, Prohibition-era beverage. Hand-crafted and handpainted, this beautiful stein is a unique interpretation of the Bevo Fox. In order to maintain the intricate detail and high quality of this special edition, only 500 steins were produced each month.

HEIGHT:
11˝
ORIGIN:
Germany
MANUFACTURER:
Thewalt & Gerz
MATERIAL:
Ceramic
LID:
Ceramic
SPECIAL FEATURES:
Individually Numbered
Certificate of Authenticity
Handpainted
Bottom Stamp
Gift Box

SIDE VIEW

DETAIL

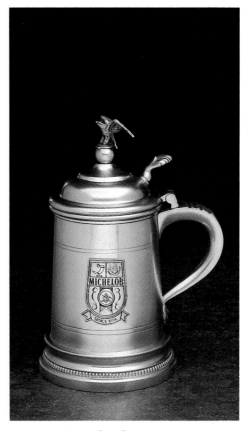

ISSUE YEAR:
1991
EDITION QUANTITY:
Open
ITEM NUMBER:
CS158

Michelob Pewter

Lidded

HEIGHT:
7¾″
ORIGIN:
USA
MANUFACTURER:
Shirley Pewter
MATERIAL:
Pewter
LID:
Pewter
SPECIAL FEATURE:
Gift Box

This American-made stein features the Michelob label graphics in a dramatic raised-pewter design. The polished pewter stein features an attractive lid topped with a powerful eagle embarking in flight. A beaded rim circles the bottom.

SIDE VIEW

DETAIL

Michelob Dry Pewter

Lidded

ISSUE YEAR:
1991
EDITION QUANTITY:
Open
ITEM NUMBER:
N2371

his American-made stein features the Michelob Dry label graphics in a dramatic raised-pewter design. The polished pewter stein features an attractive lid topped with a powerful eagle embarking in flight.

HEIGHT:
7¾″
ORIGIN:
USA
MANUFACTURER:
Shirley Pewter
MATERIAL:
Pewter
LID:
Pewter
SPECIAL FEATURE:
Gift Box

SIDE VIEW

DETAIL

ISSUE YEAR:
1991
EDITION QUANTITY:
Open
ITEM NUMBER:
N2755

Budweiser Pewter

Lidded

HEIGHT:
7¾″
ORIGIN:
USA
MANUFACTURER:
Shirley Pewter
MATERIAL:
Pewter
LID:
Pewter
SPECIAL FEATURE:
Gift Box

This American-made stein features the Budweiser label graphics in a dramatic raised-pewter design. The colonial-shaped tankard is polished pewter and features an attractive lid topped with a powerful eagle embarking in flight.

DETAIL

Budweiser Rodeo

ISSUE YEAR:
1992
EDITION QUANTITY:
Open
ITEM NUMBER:
CS184

The action-packed world of rodeo is captured on this ceramic relief open edition stein. The 5½″ stein depicts the modern day rodeo with events from steer roping to bucking broncos. To accent the subject, the stein's handle and borders are designed to resemble lasso ropes.

HEIGHT:
5½″
ORIGIN:
Brazil
MANUFACTURER:
Ceramarte
MATERIAL:
Ceramic
SPECIAL FEATURES:
Certificate of Authenticity
Bottom Stamp
Gift Box
ARTIST:
Don Langeneckert

ISSUE YEAR:
1992
EDITION QUANTITY:
Open
ITEM NUMBER:
N3289

Six Pack Mini Steins

HEIGHT:
2¼″
ORIGIN:
Chile
MANUFACTURER:
Ceramica
MATERIAL:
Ceramic

This group of six mini steins features five of Anheuser-Busch's most popular brands of beer as well as the famous A&Eagle company symbol. Brands include: Budweiser, Bud Light, Bud Dry, Busch and Michelob. The nostalgic A&Eagle rounds out the set. Original packaging includes a carrying case.

Six Pack II Mini Steins

ISSUE YEAR:
1995
EDITION QUANTITY:
Open
ITEM NUMBER:
N4571

Four more Anheuser-Busch beer brand names and two additional well-known symbols of the company are featured in this second set of six 2¼" tall mini steins. The set includes the logos of Bud Ice, King Cobra, Natural Light, Carlsberg, the Clydesdales and Bud Man. Originally packaged in a six-pack carrying case.

HEIGHT:
2¼"
ORIGIN:
Chile
MANUFACTURER:
Ceramica
MATERIAL:
Ceramic

SIDE VIEW

DETAIL

ISSUE YEAR:
1982
EDITION QUANTITY:
23,000
ITEM NUMBER:
CS53
SERIES ORDER:
First

HEIGHT:
7½″
ORIGIN:
Brazil
MANUFACTURER:
Ceramarte
MATERIAL:
Ceramic
SPECIAL FEATURES:
*Individually Numbered
Bottom Stamp*

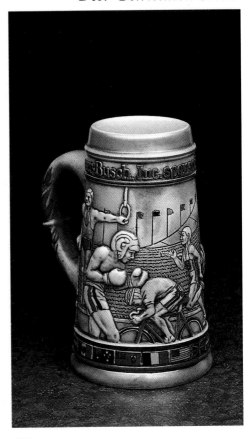

Post Convention- Olympic

This special edition stein pays tribute to the 1984 Summer Olympic Games held in Los Angeles, California. Detailed in full relief, this edition features the Budweiser logo and depicts popular Olympic events including boxing, cycling and track and field. The unique handle resembles the flame of the Olympic torch. This edition was originally distributed to Anheuser-Busch beer wholesalers only.

Post Convention Series

SIDE VIEW

DETAIL

Post Convention- Olympic

ISSUE YEAR:
1982
EDITION QUANTITY:
23,000
ITEM NUMBER:
CS54
SERIES ORDER:
Second

This special edition stein pays tribute to the 1984 Summer Olympic Games held in Los Angeles, California. Detailed in full relief, this edition features the Michelob logo and depicts Olympic events including diving, gymnastics and track and field. The unique handle resembles the flame of the Olympic torch This edition was originally distributed to Anheuser-Busch beer wholesalers only.

HEIGHT:
7½"
ORIGIN:
Brazil
MANUFACTURER:
Ceramarte
MATERIAL:
Ceramic
SPECIAL FEATURES:
Individually Numbered Bottom Stamp

Post Convention Series

SIDE VIEW

DETAIL

ISSUE YEAR:
1982
EDITION QUANTITY:
23,000
ITEM NUMBER:
CS55
SERIES ORDER:
Third

Post Convention- Olympic

HEIGHT:
10″
ORIGIN:
Brazil
MANUFACTURER:
Ceramarte
MATERIAL:
Ceramic
SPECIAL FEATURES:
*Individually Numbered
Bottom Stamp*

This special edition stein pays tribute to the 1984 Summer Olympic Games held in Los Angeles, California. Detailed in full relief, this edition features major Anheuser-Busch trademarks and the Olympic Village. The unique handle resembles the flame of the Olympic torch. This edition was originally distributed to Anheuser-Busch beer wholesalers only.

Post Convention Series

SIDE VIEW

DETAIL

Post Convention– Heritage

ISSUE YEAR:
1988
EDITION QUANTITY:
25,000
ITEM NUMBER:
CS87
SERIES ORDER:
First

This Hofbrau-style stein commemorates Adolphus Busch, President of Anheuser-Busch from 1880-1913. The attractive stein depicts the introduction of Budweiser and Michelob beers and features the trademark A&Eagle symbol. This edition was originally distributed to Anheuser-Busch beer wholesalers only.

HEIGHT:
5¼″
ORIGIN:
Gerz
MANUFACTURER:
Germany
MATERIAL:
Ceramic
SPECIAL FEATURES:
Individually Numbered Bottom Stamp

SIDE VIEW

DETAIL

ISSUE YEAR:
1988
EDITION QUANTITY:
25,000
ITEM NUMBER:
CS102
SERIES ORDER:
Second

Post Convention– Heritage

HEIGHT:
5¼″
ORIGIN:
Gerz
MANUFACTURER:
Germany
MATERIAL:
Ceramic
SPECIAL FEATURES:
Individually Numbered Bottom Stamp

This Hofbrau-style stein commemorates August Busch Sr., President of Anheuser-Busch from 1913-1934. The attractive stein depicts the company's Prohibition products and the World Famous Budweiser Clydesdales and features the trademark A&Eagle symbol. This edition was originally distributed to Anheuser-Busch beer wholesalers only.

Post Convention Series

SIDE VIEW

DETAIL

Post Convention– Heritage

ISSUE YEAR:
1989
EDITION QUANTITY:
25,000
ITEM NUMBER:
CS114
SERIES ORDER:
Third

Adolphus Busch III, President of Anheuser-Busch from 1934 to 1946, is depicted on this attractive Hofbrau-style stein. The illustration highlights the patriotic efforts of Anheuser-Busch during World War II and commemorates the company's first 300-barrel production. This stein was developed exclusively for Anheuser-Busch beer wholesalers.

HEIGHT:
5¼″
ORIGIN:
Gerz
MANUFACTURER:
Germany
MATERIAL:
Ceramic
SPECIAL FEATURES:
Individually Numbered Bottom Stamp

SIDE VIEW

DETAIL

ISSUE YEAR:
1990
EDITION QUANTITY:
25,000
ITEM NUMBER:
CS141
SERIES ORDER:
Fourth

Post Convention– Heritage

HEIGHT:
5¼″
ORIGIN:
Gerz
MANUFACTURER:
Germany
MATERIAL:
Ceramic
SPECIAL FEATURES:
Individually Numbered Bottom Stamp

The many achievements of former Anheuser-Busch President August "Gussie" Busch Jr. are chronicled on this Hofbrau-style stein. The stein's illustrations, including bottles of Budweiser, Michelob and Busch beer as well as the St. Louis Cardinals' baseball team logo, show August's accomplishments. This stein was developed exclusively for Anheuser-Busch beer wholesalers.

Post Convention Series

SIDE VIEW

DETAIL

Post Convention- Heritage

ISSUE YEAR:
1991
EDITION QUANTITY:
25,000
ITEM NUMBER:
CS174
SERIES ORDER:
Fifth & Final

This Hofbrau-style stein commemorates August A. Busch III, certified Brew Master and President of Anheuser-Busch since 1974. The stein depicts Busch's world-renowned skills as a brewer on one side and the Anheuser-Busch 140-year tradition of quality on the other. This stein was developed exclusively for Anheuser-Busch beer wholesalers.

HEIGHT:
5¼"
ORIGIN:
Gerz
MANUFACTURER:
Germany
MATERIAL:
Ceramic
SPECIAL FEATURES:
Individually Numbered Bottom Stamp

SIDE VIEW

DETAIL

ISSUE YEAR:
1992
EDITION QUANTITY:
29,000
ITEM NUMBER:
N3989
SERIES ORDER:
First

HEIGHT:
5½"
ORIGIN:
Brazil
MANUFACTURER:
Ceramarte
MATERIAL:
Ceramic
SPECIAL FEATURES:
*Individually Numbered
Bottom Stamp*

Advertising Through The Decades
1879-1912

This attractive stein depicts some of Anheuser-Busch's classic print advertisements. The vintage ads, dating from 1879-1912, are faithfully reproduced on this full relief stein. The antique design is detailed with a colorful border and sprawling red ribbon. This stein was developed exclusively for Anheuser-Busch beer wholesalers.

Post Convention Series

Advertising Through The Decades II

1905–1914

ISSUE YEAR:
1993
EDITION QUANTITY:
31,106
ITEM NUMBER:
N3990
SERIES ORDER:
Second

Second in the historical series, this antique-style, full-relief ceramic stein displays vintage Anheuser-Busch print advertisements from the years 1905 to 1914. A blue ribbon marking these years is intricately woven into the design. This stein was developed exclusively for Anheuser-Busch beer wholesalers.

HEIGHT:
5½″
ORIGIN:
Brazil
MANUFACTURER:
Ceramarte
MATERIAL:
Ceramic
SPECIAL FEATURES:
Individually Numbered Bottom Stamp

Post Convention Series

SIDE VIEW

DETAIL

ISSUE YEAR:
1994
EDITION QUANTITY:
31,000
ITEM NUMBER:
SO85203
SERIES ORDER:
Third

HEIGHT:
5½"
ORIGIN:
Brazil
MANUFACTURER:
Ceramarte
MATERIAL:
Ceramic
SPECIAL FEATURES:
Individually Numbered Bottom Stamp

Advertising Through The Decades III
1911–1915

Classic Anheuser-Busch print advertisements are once again featured on this third stein in the Advertising Through The Decades Series. In addition to the ads, which cover the years 1911 to 1915, this full-relief ceramic stein is accented by a flowing green ribbon. This stein was developed exclusively for Anheuser-Busch beer wholesalers.

Budweiser Label Series

SIDE VIEW

DETAIL

Budweiser Label

ISSUE YEAR:
1989
EDITION QUANTITY:
Open
ITEM NUMBER:
CS101
SERIES ORDER:
First

The distinct look of this Hofbrau-style stein comes from the barley and hops artwork detailed in full relief surrounding the famous Budweiser label.

HEIGHT:
5½″
ORIGIN:
Brazil
MANUFACTURER:
Ceramarte
MATERIAL:
Ceramic
SPECIAL FEATURES:
Individually Numbered
Certificate of Authenticity
Bottom Stamp
Gift Box
ARTIST:
Don Langeneckert

SIDE VIEW

DETAIL

ISSUE YEAR:
1990
EDITION QUANTITY:
Open
ITEM NUMBER:
CS127
SERIES ORDER:
Second

HEIGHT:
5½″
ORIGIN:
Brazil
MANUFACTURER:
Ceramarte
MATERIAL:
Ceramic
SPECIAL FEATURES:
Individually Numbered
Certificate of Authenticity
Bottom Stamp
Gift Box
ARTIST:
Don Langeneckert

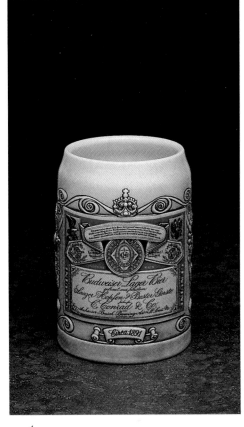

Antique Label

This stein remembers the original Budweiser label trademark featuring the authentic German inscription. The century-old label gives collectors an interesting addition to the other Budweiser Label steins.

Budweiser Label Series

SIDE VIEW

DETAIL

Budweiser Bottled Beer

ISSUE YEAR:
1991
EDITION QUANTITY:
Open
ITEM NUMBER:
CS136
SERIES ORDER:
Third

The nostalgic design of this stein is inspired by the Budweiser bottle label, circa 1890. This ceramic stein has fine relief detailing and yellow gold accents which surround the Anheuser-Busch A&Eagle logo.

HEIGHT:
5½"
ORIGIN:
Brazil
MANUFACTURER:
Ceramarte
MATERIAL:
Ceramic
SPECIAL FEATURES:
Certificate of Authenticity
Bottom Stamp
Gift Box
ARTIST:
Don Langeneckert

SIDE VIEW

DETAIL

ISSUE YEAR:
1996
EDITION QUANTITY:
Open
ITEM NUMBER:
CS282
SERIES ORDER:
Fourth

Budweiser Label

HEIGHT:
5½"
ORIGIN:
Brazil
MANUFACTURER:
Ceramarte
MATERIAL:
Ceramic
SPECIAL FEATURES:
Certificate of Authenticity
Bottom Stamp
Gift Box

Out of the rich heritage of the King of Beers comes this intricately-detailed Hofbrau-style ceramic relief stein—a tribute to Budweiser's 100-year history of quality. The world-famous Budweiser label is surrounded by detailed relief artwork of barley and hops, symbolic of Budweiser's well-known reputation for the finest quality ingredients.

Logo Series

SIDE VIEW

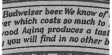

DETAIL

Budweiser Logo

ISSUE YEAR:
1990
EDITION QUANTITY:
Open
ITEM NUMBER:
CS143
SERIES ORDER:
First

This Bavarian-style flatwall stein showcases the Budweiser label graphics. Standing 5½″ tall with a half-liter capacity, this stein was introduced with Bud Light, Michelob, Michelob Dry, Busch and the A&Eagle logo steins.

HEIGHT:
5½″
ORIGIN:
Germany
MANUFACTURER:
Gerz
MATERIAL:
Ceramic

SIDE VIEW

DETAIL

ISSUE YEAR:
1990
EDITION QUANTITY:
Open
ITEM NUMBER:
CS144
SERIES ORDER:
Second

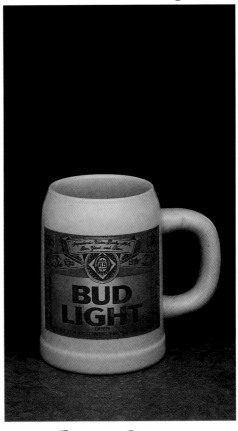

Bud Light Logo

HEIGHT:
5½″
ORIGIN:
Germany
MANUFACTURER:
Gerz
MATERIAL:
Ceramic

This Bavarian-style flatwall stein showcases the Bud Light label graphics. The 5½″ tall stein has a half-liter capacity and was introduced with Budweiser, Michelob, Michelob Dry, Busch and the A&Eagle logo steins.

Logo Series

SIDE VIEW

DETAIL

Michelob Logo

ISSUE YEAR:
1990
EDITION QUANTITY:
Open
ITEM NUMBER:
CS145
SERIES ORDER:
Third

This Bavarian-style flatwall stein showcases the Michelob label graphics. The 5½" tall stein has a half-liter capacity and was introduced with Budweiser, Bud Light, Michelob Dry, Busch and the A&Eagle logo steins.

HEIGHT:
5½"
ORIGIN:
Germany
MANUFACTURER:
Gerz
MATERIAL:
Ceramic

SIDE VIEW

DETAIL

ISSUE YEAR:
1990
EDITION QUANTITY:
Open
ITEM NUMBER:
CS146
SERIES ORDER:
Fourth

Michelob Dry Logo

HEIGHT:
5½"
ORIGIN:
Germany
MANUFACTURER:
Gerz
MATERIAL:
Ceramic

This Bavarian-style flatwall stein showcases the Michelob Dry label graphics. The 5½" tall stein has a half-liter capacity and was introduced with Budweiser, Bud Light, Michelob, Busch and the A&Eagle logo steins.

Logo Series

SIDE VIEW

DETAIL

Busch Logo

ISSUE YEAR:
1990
EDITION QUANTITY:
Open
ITEM NUMBER:
CS147
SERIES ORDER:
Fifth

This Bavarian-style flatwall stein showcases the Busch label graphics. The 5½″ tall stein has a half-liter capacity and was introduced with Budweiser, Bud Light, Michelob, Michelob Dry and the A&Eagle logo steins.

HEIGHT:
5½″
ORIGIN:
Germany
MANUFACTURER:
Gerz
MATERIAL:
Ceramic

Logo Series

SIDE VIEW

DETAIL

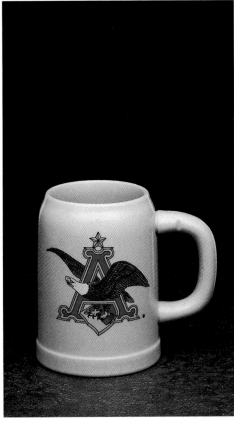

ISSUE YEAR:
1990
EDITION QUANTITY:
Open
ITEM NUMBER:
CS148
SERIES ORDER:
Sixth

A&Eagle Logo

HEIGHT:
5½″
ORIGIN:
Germany
MANUFACTURER:
Gerz
MATERIAL:
Ceramic

This Bavarian-style flatwall stein showcases the famous Anheuser-Busch A&Eagle logo. The 5½″ tall stein has a half-liter capacity and was introduced with Budweiser, Bud Light, Michelob, Michelob Dry and Busch logo steins.

Logo Series

SIDE VIEW

DETAIL

Bud Dry Logo

ISSUE YEAR:
1991
EDITION QUANTITY:
Open
ITEM NUMBER:
CS156
SERIES ORDER:
Seventh

This Bavarian-style flatwall stein showcases the Bud Dry label graphics. The 5½″ tall stein has a half-liter capacity and was manufactured after the introduction of Budweiser, Bud Light, Michelob, Michelob Dry, Busch and the A&Eagle logo steins.

HEIGHT:
5½″
ORIGIN:
Germany
MANUFACTURER:
Gerz
MATERIAL:
Ceramic

DETAIL

SIDE VIEW

ISSUE YEAR:
1991
EDITION QUANTITY:
Open
ITEM NUMBER:
N3292

Bottled Beer Stein/Tin Set

HEIGHT:
5½″
TIN DIMENSIONS:
4¾″H x 6″W x 5¾″D
ORIGIN:
Brazil
MANUFACTURER:
Ceramarte–Stein
S.A. Meister–Tin
MATERIAL:
Ceramic
SPECIAL FEATURES:
Certificate of Authenticity
Bottom Stamp
Gift Box
ARTIST:
Don Langeneckert

The A&Eagle corporate trademark is handsomely depicted on both this collectible stein and the accompanying tin. This relief design is vividly colored and beautifully shaped. The relief tin features A&Eagle logos to complement the stein.

Discover America Series

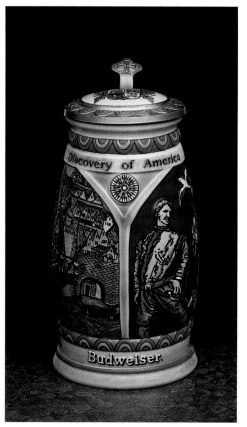

SIDE VIEW

DETAIL

Nina

ISSUE YEAR:
1990

EDITION QUANTITY:
100,000

ITEM NUMBER:
CS107

SERIES ORDER:
First

Lidded

This unique three-stein series salutes the 500th anniversary of the discovery and exploration of America. The Nina stein, decorated with rich tones and detailed artwork, chronicles Columbus' departure from Spain in 1492. Relief features include a port scene on one side and the famous Queen Isabella on the opposite side. The pewter lid is enhanced with Columbus' crest on a ceramic inlay.

HEIGHT:
8¼"

ORIGIN:
Brazil

MANUFACTURER:
Ceramarte

MATERIAL:
Ceramic

LID:
*Pewter with
Ceramic Inlay*

SPECIAL FEATURES:
*Individually Numbered
Certificate of Authenticity
Bottom Stamp
Gift Box*

Discover America Series

SIDE VIEW

DETAIL

Pinta

ISSUE YEAR:
1991
EDITION QUANTITY:
100,000
ITEM NUMBER:
CS129
SERIES ORDER:
Second

Lidded

HEIGHT:
8¼″
ORIGIN:
Brazil
MANUFACTURER:
Ceramarte
MATERIAL:
Ceramic
LID:
*Pewter with
Ceramic Inlay*
SPECIAL FEATURES:
*Individually Numbered
Certificate of Authenticity
Bottom Stamp
Gift Box*

This historical stein captures the essence of the long and trying journey Columbus made as he crossed the globe in search of new lands. The ship is shown in the dark of night with deep blues and bright stars. The second in the series, the Pinta stein is crafted in detailed medieval-style relief featuring a unique pewter lid with a ceramic inlay of Columbus' crest.

Discover America Series

SIDE VIEW

DETAIL

Santa Maria

Lidded

ISSUE YEAR:
1992
EDITION QUANTITY:
100,000
ITEM NUMBER:
CS138
SERIES ORDER:
Third & Final

The final stein in the Discover America series commemorates Columbus and his men as they landed on American shores. Rich blues and browns accent the sailing ship Santa Maria on the other side of the stein. Handcrafted in detailed medieval-style relief, the stein also has a distinctive pewter lid with a ceramic inlay of Columbus' crest.

HEIGHT:
8¼″
ORIGIN:
Brazil
MANUFACTURER:
Ceramarte
MATERIAL:
Ceramic
LID:
Pewter with Ceramic Inlay
SPECIAL FEATURES:
Individually Numbered
Certificate of Authenticity
Bottom Stamp
Gift Box

SIDE VIEW

DETAIL

Erin Go Bud

ISSUE YEAR:
1991
EDITION QUANTITY:
25,000
ITEM NUMBER:
CS109
SERIES ORDER:
First

HEIGHT:
5½″
ORIGIN:
Brazil
MANUFACTURER:
Ceramarte
MATERIAL:
Ceramic
SPECIAL FEATURE:
Bottom Stamp
ARTIST:
Tom Patrick

This is the first in the Budweiser St. Patrick's Day series of holiday steins. The colorful design, detailed in full relief, shows a festive holiday scene complete with leprechauns and a delicious mug of ice cold Budweiser.

St. Patrick's Day Series

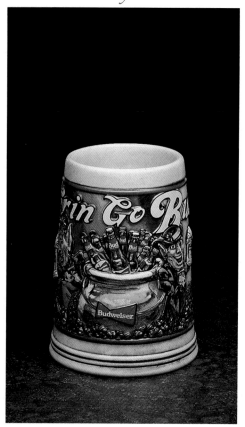

SIDE VIEW

DETAIL

Pot of Gold

ISSUE YEAR:
1992
EDITION QUANTITY:
100,000
ITEM NUMBER:
CS166
SERIES ORDER:
Second

This stein is the second in the Anheuser-Busch St. Patrick's Day series. The colorful relief stein shows a lucky leprechaun who has followed the rainbow to find a pot of gold filled with bottles of Budweiser. The festive greeting "Erin Go Bud" and shamrock thumbrest complete the St. Patrick's Day celebration.

HEIGHT:
5½"
ORIGIN:
Brazil
MANUFACTURER:
Ceramarte
MATERIAL:
Ceramic
SPECIAL FEATURES:
*Certificate of Authenticity
Bottom Stamp*
ARTIST:
Marcy Wilson

St. Patrick's Day Series

SIDE VIEW

DETAIL

ISSUE YEAR:
1993
EDITION QUANTITY:
50,000
ITEM NUMBER:
CS193
SERIES ORDER:
Third

Bottled Treasure

HEIGHT:
5½″
ORIGIN:
Brazil
MANUFACTURER:
Ceramarte
MATERIAL:
Ceramic
SPECIAL FEATURES:
Certificate of Authenticity
Bottom Stamp
Gift Box
ARTIST:
Michael Lynch

Bottled Treasure, the third in the Anheuser-Busch series of St. Patrick's Day steins, celebrates the Irish spirit. The humorous stein shows a scene of a trio of leprechauns who have found a real treasure under the rainbow: an icy bottle of Budweiser. As with the two previous steins in the series, Bottled Treasure features the festive "Erin Go Bud" greeting.

St. Patrick's Day Series

SIDE VIEW

DETAIL

Luck O' The Irish

ISSUE YEAR:
1994
EDITION QUANTITY:
Open
ITEM NUMBER:
CS210
SERIES ORDER:
Fourth

Luck O' the Irish is the fourth Budweiser St. Patrick's Day stein. This leprechaun's pot is full of much more than just gold—ice cold cans of Budweiser, too! The unique and colorful design is expertly reproduced in full, detailed relief. A shamrock handle adds another interesting touch.

HEIGHT:
5¾"
ORIGIN:
Brazil
MANUFACTURER:
Ceramarte
MATERIAL:
Ceramic
SPECIAL FEATURES:
Certificate of Authenticity
Bottom Stamp
Gift Box

St. Patrick's Day Series

SIDE VIEW

DETAIL

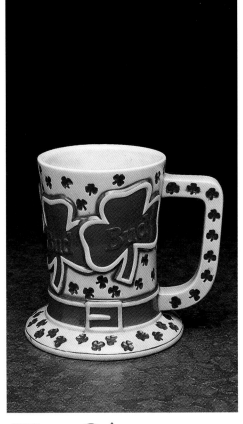

ISSUE YEAR:
1995
EDITION QUANTITY:
Open
ITEM NUMBER:
CS242
SERIES ORDER:
Fifth

Tip O' The Hat

HEIGHT:
5¾″
ORIGIN:
Brazil
MANUFACTURER:
Ceramarte
MATERIAL:
Ceramic
SPECIAL FEATURES:
Certificate of Authenticity
Bottom Stamp
Gift Box

This fifth stein in the Budweiser St. Patrick's Day series is cleverly designed in the shape of a leprechaun's hat. Giant emerald-green shamrocks in full relief feature the word "Bud" in bright red. In addition, a pattern of miniature shamrocks covers the entire stein, as well as the handle.

St. Patrick's Day Series

SIDE VIEW

DETAIL

1996 St. Patrick's Day Horseshoe

ISSUE YEAR:
1996
EDITION QUANTITY:
Open
ITEM NUMBER:
CS269
SERIES ORDER:
Sixth

The on-going St. Patrick's Day series continues with this beautiful sixth edition. The world-famous Budweiser Clydesdales are featured in dramatic full-color relief, as they high-step their way through a stylized horseshoe. The striking illustration is complemented by a unique horseshoe-shaped handle.

HEIGHT:
5½"
ORIGIN:
Brazil
MANUFACTURER:
Ceramarte
MATERIAL:
Ceramic
SPECIAL FEATURES:
Certificate of Authenticity
Bottom Stamp
Gift Box
ARTIST:
Geoff Greenleaf

SIDE VIEW

DETAIL

ISSUE YEAR:
1992
EDITION QUANTITY:
25,000
ITEM NUMBER:
CS181
SERIES ORDER:
First

General Ulysses S. Grant

Lidded

HEIGHT:
12½"
ORIGIN:
Brazil
MANUFACTURER:
Ceramarte
MATERIAL:
Ceramic
LID & BASE:
Pewter
SPECIAL FEATURES:
Individually Numbered
Certificate of Authenticity
Bottom Stamp
Gift Box
ARTIST:
Don Langeneckert

This dramatic stein salutes Civil War hero General Ulysses S. Grant whose relief portrait highlights the front. The handcrafted stein recounts such milestones as the Battles of Shiloh and Vicksburg and the attack on Fort Donelson. The spectacular pewter lid stands 5½" tall and is shaped like the U.S. Capitol rotunda, topped with the figurine of Grant in uniform.

165

Civil War Series

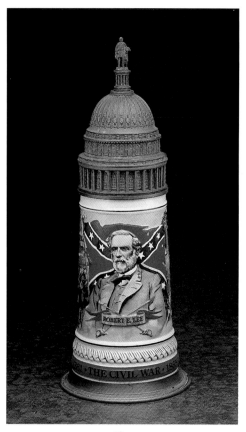

SIDE VIEW

DETAIL

General Robert E. Lee

Lidded

ISSUE YEAR:
1993
EDITION QUANTITY:
25,000
ITEM NUMBER:
CS188
SERIES ORDER:
Second

The second stein in this historic Civil War series salutes Southern leader General Robert E. Lee depicted on the relief front panel. His portrait is surrounded by images recalling the events of Fort Sumter, Pickett's Charge and the Battle of Gettysburg. The solid pewter lid stands 5½″ tall and is shaped like the U.S. Capitol rotunda, topped with the figurine of Lee in uniform.

HEIGHT:
12½″
ORIGIN:
Brazil
MANUFACTURER:
Ceramarte
MATERIAL:
Ceramic
LID & BASE:
Pewter
SPECIAL FEATURES:
Individually Numbered
Certificate of Authenticity
Bottom Stamp
Gift Box
ARTIST:
Don Langeneckert

SIDE VIEW

DETAIL

ISSUE YEAR:
1993
EDITION QUANTITY:
25,000
ITEM NUMBER:
CS189
SERIES ORDER:
Third & Final

Abraham Lincoln

Lidded

HEIGHT:
12½″
ORIGIN:
Brazil
MANUFACTURER:
Ceramarte
MATERIAL:
Ceramic
LID:
Pewter
SPECIAL FEATURES:
Individually Numbered
Certificate of Authenticity
Bottom Stamp
Gift Box
ARTIST:
Don Langeneckert

President Abraham Lincoln is honored on the third and final stein in Anheuser-Busch's Commemorative Civil War series. The relief stein depicts Lincoln in a montage of scenes that represent the tumultuous events of his presidency. In addition, this edition features a 5½″ tall pewter lid shaped like the U.S. Capitol rotunda topped with a figurine of President Lincoln.

Budweiser Salutes the Military Series

SIDE VIEW

DETAIL

Budweiser Salutes the Army

ISSUE YEAR:
1994
EDITION QUANTITY:
Open
ITEM NUMBER:
CS224
SERIES ORDER:
First

The first stein in our Budweiser Salutes the Military Series honors the fighting forces of the U.S. Army. A detailed full-color illustration by artist Mark Watts is a dramatic collage of battle scenes showing today's army in action. The stein is accented by metallic top and bottom bands, the Budweiser logo, the Army mascot and a bullet-shaped handle.

HEIGHT:
6¼"
ORIGIN:
Brazil
MANUFACTURER:
Ceramarte
MATERIAL:
Ceramic
SPECIAL FEATURES:
Certificate of Authenticity
Bottom Stamp
Gift Box
ARTIST:
Mark Watts

Budweiser Salutes the Military Series

SIDE VIEW

DETAIL

ISSUE YEAR:
1994
EDITION QUANTITY:
Open
ITEM NUMBER:
CS228
SERIES ORDER:
Second

Budweiser Salutes the Air Force

HEIGHT:
6¼″
ORIGIN:
Brazil
MANUFACTURER:
Ceramarte
MATERIAL:
Ceramic
SPECIAL FEATURES:
*Certificate of Authenticity
Bottom Stamp
Gift Box*
ARTIST:
Mark Watts

The Air Force is the second branch of American armed forces to be featured in the Budweiser Salutes the Military Series. Artist Mark Watts' striking full-color rendering depicts fighter planes, pilots and ground support in action. The handle is in the form of a plane's control stick. Other distinguishing features include metallic bands, a Budweiser logo and the Air Force mascot.

Budweiser Salutes the Military Series

SIDE VIEW

DETAIL

Budweiser Salutes the Navy

ISSUE YEAR:
1995
EDITION QUANTITY:
Open
ITEM NUMBER:
CS243
SERIES ORDER:
Third

A tribute to the men and women of the U.S. Navy, this stein is the third in the Budweiser Salutes the Military Series. The brilliant talent of artist Mark Watts is again displayed in an illustration of naval sea and air operations. Anchor chains are featured in two metallic bands and as the shape of the handle. The Budweiser logo and Navy mascot are also shown.

HEIGHT:
6¼"
ORIGIN:
Brazil
MANUFACTURER:
Ceramarte
MATERIAL:
Ceramic
SPECIAL FEATURES:
Certificate of Authenticity
Bottom Stamp
Gift Box
ARTIST:
Mark Watts

Budweiser Salutes the Military Series

SIDE VIEW

DETAIL

ISSUE YEAR:
1995
EDITION QUANTITY:
Open
ITEM NUMBER:
CS256
SERIES ORDER:
Fourth

Budweiser Salutes the Marines

HEIGHT:
6¼"
ORIGIN:
Brazil
MANUFACTURER:
Ceramarte
MATERIAL:
Ceramic
SPECIAL FEATURES:
*Certificate of Authenticity
Bottom Stamp
Gift Box*
ARTIST:
Mark Watts

Our Budweiser Salutes the Military Series continues with this fourth edition honoring the U.S. Marine Corps. Another exceptional illustration by artist Mark Watts depicts brave Marines engaged in intense landing operations. Signature swords in metallic bands are featured with the Budweiser logo and the Marines bulldog mascot. The unique handle is that of a sword.

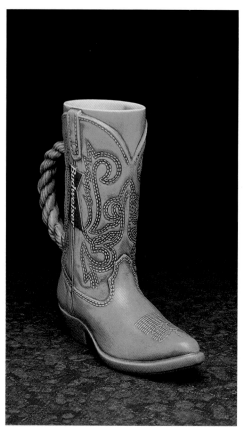

DETAIL

Cowboy Boot

ISSUE YEAR:
1994
EDITION QUANTITY:
Open
ITEM NUMBER:
CS251

A tribute to the American cowboy, this 8¼" tall stein features 3-dimensional ceramic relief. Authentic detail includes a handle that appears to be a lasso. The red Budweiser bowtie logo runs vertically down the sides of the stein.

HEIGHT:
8¼"
ORIGIN:
Brazil
MANUFACTURER:
Ceramarte
MATERIAL:
Ceramic
SPECIAL FEATURES:
Certificate of Authenticity
Bottom Stamp
Gift Box

SIDE VIEW

DETAIL

ISSUE YEAR:
1994
EDITION QUANTITY:
Open
ITEM NUMBER:
CS225

Budweiser Golf Bag

HEIGHT:
6¾″
ORIGIN:
Brazil
MANUFACTURER:
Ceramarte
MATERIAL:
Ceramic
SPECIAL FEATURES:
Certificate of Authenticity
Bottom Stamp
Gift Box

This unique 3-dimensional stein is shaped to resemble an actual Budweiser pro golf bag. The 6¾″ tall stein features detailed ceramic relief in black, with bright red Budweiser and Bud King of Beers logos.

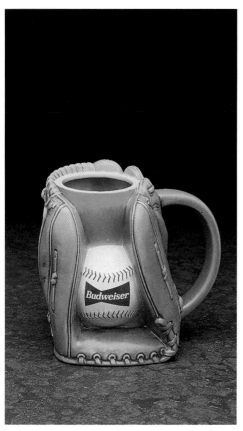

SIDE VIEW

DETAIL

Baseball Mitt

ISSUE YEAR:
1995
EDITION QUANTITY:
Open
ITEM NUMBER:
CS244

Another uniquely-shaped, three-dimensional design, this detailed relief stein looks just like an actual baseball mitt. Extremely authentic, the 6¾" tall stein even features a baseball in the mitt, complete with a bright red Budweiser bowtie logo.

HEIGHT:
6¾"
ORIGIN:
Brazil
MANUFACTURER:
Ceramarte
MATERIAL:
Ceramic
SPECIAL FEATURES:
Certificate of Authenticity
Bottom Stamp
Gift Box

SIDE VIEW

DETAIL

ISSUE YEAR:
1996
EDITION QUANTITY:
Open
ITEM NUMBER:
CS278

Billiards

HEIGHT:
6"
ORIGIN:
Brazil
MANUFACTURER:
Ceramarte
MATERIAL:
Ceramic
SPECIAL FEATURES:
Certificate of Authenticity
Bottom Stamp
Gift Box

Circling the entire body of this 6" tall relief stein is the unmistakable green felt top of a pool table. Several balls are scattered around the familiar bright red "Budweiser" which runs the entire length of the table. An impressive handle—a detailed replica of a pool cue—completes the picture.

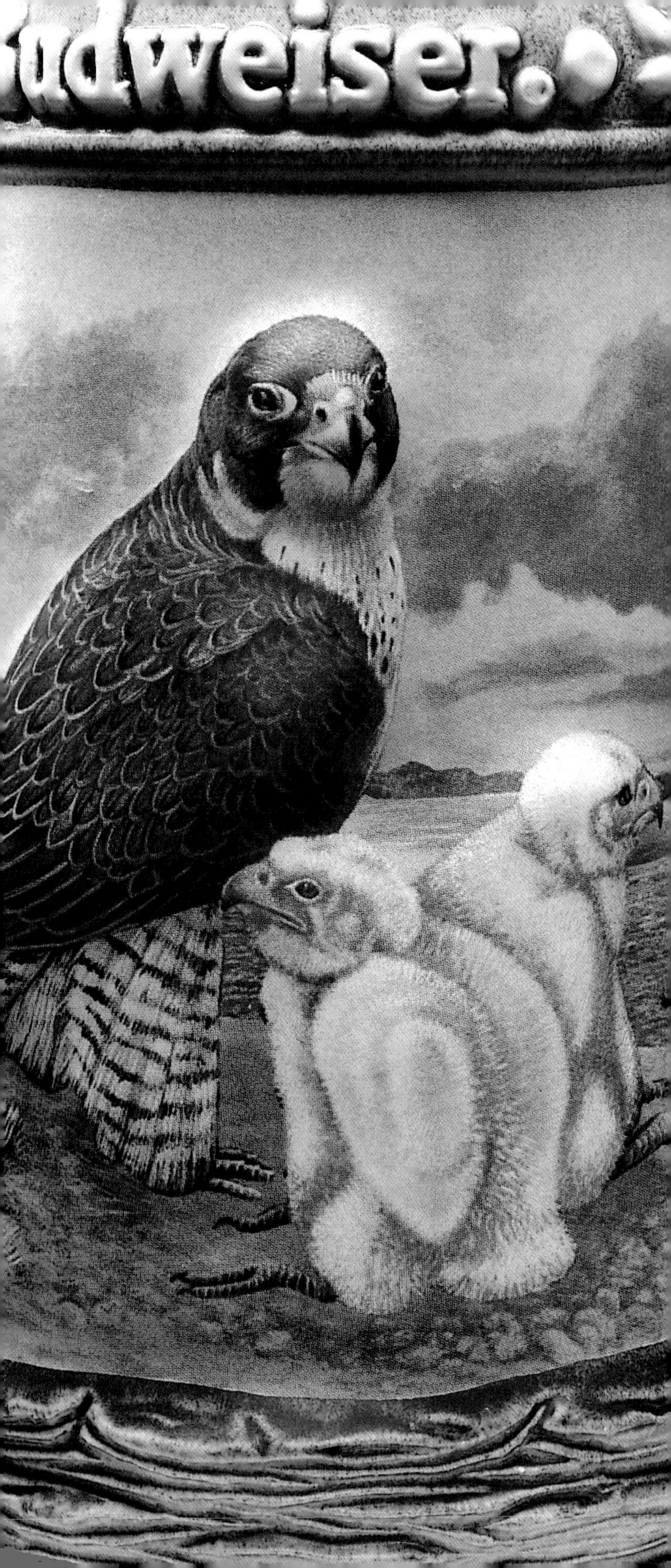
udweiser.

Animals & Wildlife Steins

This section represents those steins depicting animals and wildlife, many of which are in danger of extinction. Artfully illustrated and colored, these beautiful animals are depicted in their natural habitats. In addition to helping educate collectors about the endangered species, Anheuser-Busch donates contributions to a number of wildlife conservation groups. ∽

Animals & Wildlife Steins

Contents of This Section

ISSUE YEAR:
1988
EDITION QUANTITY:
Open
ITEM NUMBER:
CS95

Budweiser Field & Stream Set

HEIGHT:
5½″
SHELF DIMENSIONS:
6¾″H x 18¾″W x 7″D
ORIGIN:
Brazil
MANUFACTURER:
Ceramarte
MATERIAL:
Ceramic
SPECIAL FEATURES:
Bottom Stamp
Wood Display Shelf

Budweiser's Field & Steam set includes four steins featuring artwork of North American fish and game. The lively and colorful illustrations include scenes of bear, deer, fish and fowl. The four steins were introduced as a set in 1988 and also included a wood display shelf.

©Field & Stream is a trademark of Times Mirror Magazine, Inc. used under license by Anheuser-Busch, Inc.

SIDE VIEW

DETAIL

Killer Whale

Lidded

ISSUE YEAR:
1992
EDITION QUANTITY:
25,000
ITEM NUMBER:
CS186

This limited edition Killer Whale stein has been designed exclusively for Sea World, Inc., a subsidiary of Anheuser-Busch Companies, Inc. The colorful ceramic relief shows the distinctive black and white killer whale gliding through deep waters. The pewter thumbrest is crafted to resemble the whale's tail rising above the sea.

HEIGHT:
9¼"
ORIGIN:
Germany
MANUFACTURER:
Gerz
MATERIAL:
Ceramic
LID:
Pewter
SPECIAL FEATURES:
Individually Numbered
Certificate of Authenticity
Bottom Stamp
Gift Box

SIDE VIEW

DETAIL

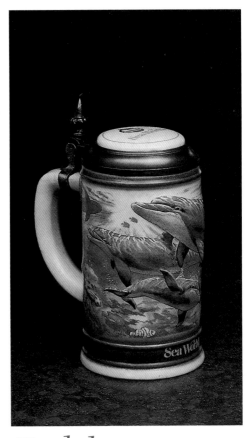

ISSUE YEAR:
1992
EDITION QUANTITY:
22,500
ITEM NUMBER:
CS187

Dolphin

Lidded

HEIGHT:
7¼″
ORIGIN:
Germany
MANUFACTURER:
Gerz
MATERIAL:
Ceramic
LID:
*Pewter with
Ceramic Inlay*
SPECIAL FEATURES:
*Individually Numbered
Certificate of Authenticity
Bottom Stamp
Gift Box*

This detailed relief stein honors the dolphin, considered to be one of the ocean's most playful and gentle inhabitants. The dolphin's underwater antics come to life in a sea of rich blues. The 7¼″ stein, designed especially for Sea World, Inc., a subsidiary of Anheuser-Busch Companies, Inc., is topped by a pewter lid with ceramic inlay. Dolphin fins create the thumbrest.

Hunter's Companion Series

SIDE VIEW

DETAIL

Labrador

Lidded

ISSUE YEAR:
1993
EDITION QUANTITY:
50,000
ITEM NUMBER:
CS195
SERIES ORDER:
First

The Labrador stein is the first edition in the Hunter's Companion series. The relief design is colored in outdoor blues, greens and yellows, giving perfect contrast to the deep black Labrador. Two sides of the loyal Labrador retriever are depicted: working hard in the field and at attention. The unique pewter lid features a ceramic Labrador figurine on top.

HEIGHT:
8¼"
ORIGIN:
Brazil
MANUFACTURER:
Ceramarte
MATERIAL:
Ceramic
LID:
Pewter with Ceramic Figurine
SPECIAL FEATURES:
Individually Numbered Certificate of Authenticity Bottom Stamp Gift Box
ARTIST:
Leonard Freeman

Hunter's Companion Series

SIDE VIEW

DETAIL

ISSUE YEAR:
1994
EDITION QUANTITY:
50,000
ITEM NUMBER:
CS205
SERIES ORDER:
Second

Setter

Lidded

HEIGHT:
8¼″
ORIGIN:
Brazil
MANUFACTURER:
Ceramarte
MATERIAL:
Ceramic
LID:
Pewter with Ceramic Figurine
SPECIAL FEATURES:
Individually Numbered Certificate of Authenticity Bottom Stamp Gift Box
ARTIST:
Susan Ryan

A trio of intelligent hunters—the English, Gordon and Irish setters—are the subjects of this second stein in the Hunter's Companion Series. The first of artist Susan Ryan's striking renderings for the series shows all three of these beautiful animals intensely focused on the hunt. A ceramic Irish setter figurine sits atop the pewter-rimmed lid.

Hunter's Companion Series

SIDE VIEW

DETAIL

Golden Retriever

Lidded

ISSUE YEAR:
1995
EDITION QUANTITY:
50,000
ITEM NUMBER:
CS248
SERIES ORDER:
Third

The third edition in the Anheuser-Busch Hunter's Companion Series is a stunning salute to the loyal golden retriever. Artist Susan Ryan's beautifully rendered, ceramic relief scenes features the retriever at his master's side and in the field. The unique pewter-rimmed lid is topped with a ceramic golden retriever figurine on top.

HEIGHT:
8¼"
ORIGIN:
Brazil
MANUFACTURER:
Ceramarte
MATERIAL:
Ceramic
LID:
Pewter with Ceramic Figurine
SPECIAL FEATURES:
Individually Numbered Certificate of Authenticity Bottom Stamp Gift Box
ARTIST:
Susan Ryan

Hunter's Companion Series

SIDE VIEW

DETAIL

ISSUE YEAR:
1996

EDITION QUANTITY:
50,000

ITEM NUMBER:
CS272

SERIES ORDER:
Fourth

Beagle

Lidded

HEIGHT:
8¼″

ORIGIN:
Brazil

MANUFACTURER:
Ceramarte

MATERIAL:
Ceramic

LID:
*Pewter with
Ceramic Figurine*

SPECIAL FEATURES:
*Individually Numbered
Certificate of Authenticity
Bottom Stamp
Gift Box*

ARTIST:
Susan Ryan

The fourth stein in our Hunter's Companion Series honors the popular beagle. Another exceptional illustration from artist Susan Ryan is brilliantly reproduced in full relief. A large, detailed rendering of a traditional beagle is centered between two additional scenes of beagles in the field. The engraved pewter-rimmed lid features a ceramic beagle figurine.

Endangered Species Series

SIDE VIEW

DETAIL

Bald Eagle

Lidded

ISSUE YEAR:
1989
EDITION QUANTITY:
100,000
ITEM NUMBER:
CS106
SERIES ORDER:
First

Anheuser-Busch draws attention to the importance of saving the world's endangered species in this unique stein series. The bald eagle, symbol of the United States, is featured soaring and in profile on this lavishly illustrated stein. A handsome ceramic inlaid lid tops the stein. Anheuser-Busch has donated a portion of the sale of each stein to the National Wildlife Federation.

HEIGHT:
6½"
ORIGIN:
Brazil
MANUFACTURER:
Ceramarte
MATERIAL:
Ceramic
LID:
Pewter with Ceramic Inlay
SPECIAL FEATURES:
Individually Numbered
Certificate of Authenticity
Bottom Stamp
Gift Box
ARTIST:
Bud Kemper

Endangered Species Series

SIDE VIEW

DETAIL

YEAR:
1990
EDITION QUANTITY:
100,000
ITEM NUMBER:
CS126
SERIES ORDER:
Second

Asian Tiger

Lidded

HEIGHT:
6½"
ORIGIN:
Brazil
MANUFACTURER:
Ceramarte
MATERIAL:
Ceramic
LID:
Pewter with Ceramic Inlay
SPECIAL FEATURES:
Individually Numbered Certificate of Authenticity Bottom Stamp Gift Box
ARTIST:
Bud Kemper

The second stein in the Anheuser-Busch Endangered Species Series features the Asian tiger. Artist Bud Kemper has captured the spirit of this noble jungle hunter in a truly remarkable rendering. The stein's pewter lid includes a full-color ceramic inlay. Anheuser-Busch has donated a portion of the sale of each stein to the National Wildlife Federation.

Endangered Species Series

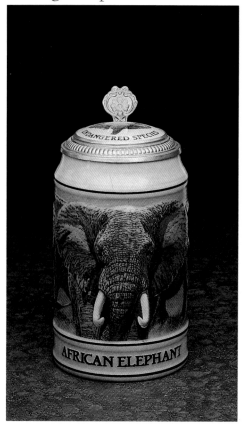

SIDE VIEW

DETAIL

African Elephant

Lidded

YEAR:
1991
EDITION QUANTITY:
100,000
ITEM NUMBER:
CS135
SERIES ORDER:
Third

The African elephant is the subject of this third stein in the popular series. Featured in its natural African plains habitat, this member of the world's endangered species list has been dramatically illustrated in full color. The stein also features a ceramic inlaid lid. Anheuser-Busch has donated a portion of the sale of each stein to the National Wildlife Federation.

HEIGHT:
6½"
ORIGIN:
Brazil
MANUFACTURER:
Ceramarte
MATERIAL:
Ceramic
LID:
Pewter with Ceramic Inlay
SPECIAL FEATURES:
Individually Numbered Certificate of Authenticity Bottom Stamp Gift Box
ARTIST:
Bud Kemper

SIDE VIEW

DETAIL

ISSUE YEAR:
1992
EDITION QUANTITY:
100,000
ITEM NUMBER:
CS173
SERIES ORDER:
Fourth

Giant Panda

Lidded

HEIGHT:
6½″
ORIGIN:
Brazil
MANUFACTURER:
Ceramarte
MATERIAL:
Ceramic
LID:
*Pewter with
Ceramic Inlay*
SPECIAL FEATURES:
*Individually Numbered
Certificate of Authenticity
Bottom Stamp
Gift Box*
ARTIST:
Bud Kemper

A favorite of Anheuser-Busch stein collectors, the Endangered Species Series continues with the addition of the giant panda. This famous native of southeast China is depicted in its natural habitat. The panda illustration is again featured on a ceramic inlay in the stein's pewter lid. Anheuser-Busch has donated a portion of the sale of each stein to the National Wildlife Federation.

Endangered Species Series

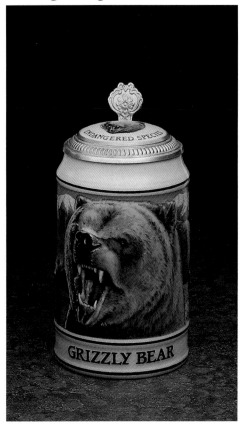

SIDE VIEW

DETAIL

Grizzly Bear

Lidded

S tein number five in the Endangered Species Series features the fierce but beautiful grizzly bear. Detailed illustrations by artist Bud Kemper show a dramatic growling grizzly, contrasted by a relaxed grizzly with its cub. A pewter lid with a ceramic inlay tops off the stein. Anheuser-Busch has donated a portion of the sale of each stein to the National Wildlife Federation.

ISSUE YEAR:
1993
EDITION QUANTITY:
100,000
ITEM NUMBER:
CS199
SERIES ORDER:
Fifth

HEIGHT:
6½"
ORIGIN:
Brazil
MANUFACTURER:
Ceramarte
MATERIAL:
Ceramic
LID:
Pewter with Ceramic Inlay
SPECIAL FEATURES:
Individually Numbered Certificate of Authenticity Bottom Stamp Gift Box
ARTIST:
Bud Kemper

SIDE VIEW

DETAIL

ISSUE YEAR:
1994
EDITION QUANTITY:
100,000
ITEM NUMBER:
CS226
SERIES ORDER:
Sixth

Gray Wolf

Lidded

HEIGHT:
6½″
ORIGIN:
Brazil
MANUFACTURER:
Ceramarte
MATERIAL:
Ceramic
LID:
*Pewter with
Ceramic Inlay*
SPECIAL FEATURES:
*Individually Numbered
Certificate of Authenticity
Bottom Stamp
Gift Box*
ARTIST:
Bud Kemper

The sixth edition of the long-running Endangered Species Series draws attention to the stunning gray wolf. Illustrated in its typical wooded habitat, the gray wolf is highlighted by its notoriously piercing eyes. The stein also features a ceramic inlaid lid. Anheuser-Busch has donated a portion of the sale of each stein to the National Wildlife Federation.

Endangered Species Series

SIDE VIEW

DETAIL

Cougar

Lidded

ISSUE YEAR:
1995
EDITION QUANTITY:
100,000
ITEM NUMBER:
CS253
SERIES ORDER:
Seventh

Another of the world's many endangered species is featured in this seventh stein in the series. The cougar, a slender but powerful cat, is beautifully illustrated by series artist Bud Kemper. The trademark ceramic inlaid lid with full-color illustration tops the stein. Anheuser-Busch has donated a portion of the sale of each stein to the National Wildlife Federation.

HEIGHT:
6½"
ORIGIN:
Brazil
MANUFACTURER:
Ceramarte
MATERIAL:
Ceramic
LID:
Pewter with Ceramic Inlay
SPECIAL FEATURES:
Individually Numbered Certificate of Authenticity Bottom Stamp Gift Box
ARTIST:
Bud Kemper

SIDE VIEW

DETAIL

ISSUE YEAR:
1991
EDITION QUANTITY:
25,000
ITEM NUMBER:
CS164
SERIES ORDER:
First

American Bald Eagle

Lidded

HEIGHT:
10½″
ORIGIN:
Germany
MANUFACTURER:
Gerz
MATERIAL:
Ceramic
LID:
Pewter
SPECIAL FEATURES:
*Individually Numbered
Certificate of Authenticity
Bottom Stamp
Gift Box*
ARTIST:
Pat Ford

The first stein in the impressive Birds of Prey series pays tribute to the American bald eagle. The majestic illustration captures this regal bird surveying its domain high above a mountain habitat. The wilderness theme is heightened with a finely crafted tree trunk handle and leaf thumbrest. With each purchase, Anheuser-Busch made a donation to the World Bird Sanctuary.

Birds of Prey Series

SIDE VIEW

DETAIL

Peregrine Falcon

Lidded

ISSUE YEAR:
1992
EDITION QUANTITY:
25,000
ITEM NUMBER:
CS183
SERIES ORDER:
Second

Made of fine ceramic adorned with vivid colors, the Peregrine Falcon stein displays stunning artwork and features an impressive three-dimensional A&Eagle pewter figurine on the lid. This detailed stein shows views of this noble bird in flight and calmly perched. Anheuser-Busch made a donation to the World Bird Sanctuary with each purchase.

HEIGHT:
10½″
ORIGIN:
Germany
MANUFACTURER:
Gerz
MATERIAL:
Ceramic
LID:
Pewter
SPECIAL FEATURES:
Individually Numbered
Certificate of Authenticity
Bottom Stamp
Gift Box
ARTIST:
Pat Ford

Birds of Prey Series

SIDE VIEW

DETAIL

ISSUE YEAR:
1994
EDITION QUANTITY:
25,000
ITEM NUMBER:
CS212
SERIES ORDER:
Third

Osprey

Lidded

HEIGHT:
10½″
ORIGIN:
Germany
MANUFACTURER:
Gerz
MATERIAL:
Ceramic
LID:
Pewter
SPECIAL FEATURES:
*Individually Numbered
Certificate of Authenticity
Bottom Stamp
Gift Box*
ARTIST:
Pat Ford

Marking the third edition in the Birds of Prey Series, this exquisite full relief stein features the majestic osprey. Also known as a fish hawk, this large hunter is shown cruising above the water and plunging to take its prey. The stein features a solid pewter lid with a sculpted A&Eagle figurine. Anheuser-Busch donates a portion of each sale to the World Bird Sanctuary.

Birds of Prey Series

SIDE VIEW

DETAIL

Great Horned Owl

Lidded

ISSUE YEAR:
1995
EDITION QUANTITY:
25,000
ITEM NUMBER:
CS264
SERIES ORDER:
Fourth

The fourth and final edition of the Birds of Prey Series features the great horned owl, a formidable night hunter. The bird's sharp-eyed face, finely feathered body and deep forest habitat are all beautifully illustrated in full relief. The solid pewter lid with sculpted A&Eagle figurine is a hallmark of the series. A portion of each sale was donated to the World Bird Sanctuary.

HEIGHT:
10½"
ORIGIN:
Germany
MANUFACTURER:
Gerz
MATERIAL:
Ceramic
LID:
Pewter
SPECIAL FEATURES:
Individually Numbered
Certificate of Authenticity
Bottom Stamp
Gift Box
ARTIST:
Pat Ford

Marine Conservation Series

SIDE VIEW

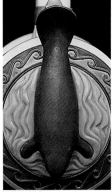

DETAIL

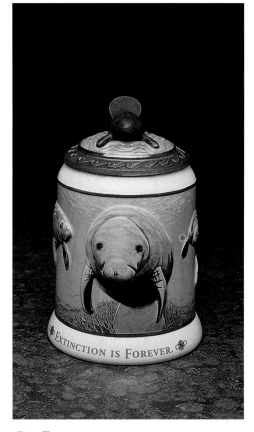

ISSUE YEAR:
1994
EDITION QUANTITY:
25,000
ITEM NUMBER:
CS203
SERIES ORDER:
First

Manatee

Lidded

HEIGHT:
6½″
ORIGIN:
Brazil
MANUFACTURER:
Ceramarte
MATERIAL:
Ceramic
LID:
*Pewter with Figurine
and Ceramic Inlay*
SPECIAL FEATURES:
*Individually Numbered
Certificate of Authenticity
Bottom Stamp
Gift Box*
ARTIST:
Bud Kemper

The first stein in our Marine Conservation Series, beautifully illustrated by renowned artist Bud Kemper, features the gentle manatee in full-color ceramic relief. The pewter lid has a detailed ceramic inlay topped with a manatee figurine—with the tail becoming the thumbrest.

Marine Conservation Series

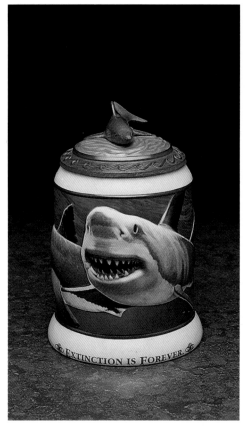

SIDE VIEW

DETAIL

Great White Shark

Lidded

ISSUE YEAR:
1995
EDITION QUANTITY:
25,000
ITEM NUMBER:
CS247
SERIES ORDER:
Second

The large and powerful great white shark is the subject of this second Marine Conservation Series stein. Bud Kemper's outstanding artwork, reproduced in full-color relief, captures the dominating presence of the great white. A shark figurine atop the ceramic inlaid pewter lid also acts as the thumbrest.

HEIGHT:
6½"
ORIGIN:
Brazil
MANUFACTURER:
Ceramarte
MATERIAL:
Ceramic
LID:
Pewter with Figurine and Ceramic Inlay
SPECIAL FEATURES:
*Individually Numbered
Certificate of Authenticity
Bottom Stamp
Gift Box*
ARTIST:
Bud Kemper

Busch Gardens Extinction is Forever Series

SIDE VIEW

DETAIL

ISSUE YEAR:
1985
EDITION QUANTITY:
10,000
ITEM NUMBER:
Not available
SERIES ORDER:
First

Busch Gardens Extinction is Forever I

HEIGHT:
6¼"
ORIGIN:
Brazil
MANUFACTURER:
Ceramarte
MATERIAL:
Ceramic
SPECIAL FEATURES:
Bottom Stamp
Gift Box
ARTIST:
Jerry Lundwall

The Busch Gardens Extinction is Forever Series, was begun to celebrate Busch Garden's efforts to preserve our environment. This first stein in the series features a beautiful full-color rendering that includes many of the wild animals that roam free in the popular theme park.

Busch Gardens Extinction is Forever Series

SIDE VIEW

DETAIL

Busch Gardens Extinction is Forever II

ISSUE YEAR:
1990
EDITION QUANTITY:
10,000
ITEM NUMBER:
BG1
SERIES ORDER:
Second

Second in the Busch Gardens Extinction is Forever Series, this stein features a detailed illustration of the wide variety of wild animals that inhabit the famous 300-acre African theme park in Tampa, Florida. The series was designed to salute the park's efforts to preserve our environment.

HEIGHT:
6¼"
ORIGIN:
Brazil
MANUFACTURER:
Ceramarte
MATERIAL:
Ceramic
SPECIAL FEATURES:
Bottom Stamp
Gift Box
ARTIST:
Russ Kramer

Busch Gardens Extinction is Forever Series

SIDE VIEW

DETAIL

ISSUE YEAR:
1992
EDITION QUANTITY:
10,000
ITEM NUMBER:
BG2
SERIES ORDER:
Third

Busch Gardens Extinction is Forever III

HEIGHT:
7½"
ORIGIN:
Brazil
MANUFACTURER:
Ceramarte
MATERIAL:
Ceramic
LID:
Pewter with Ceramic Inlay
SPECIAL FEATURES:
*Bottom Stamp
Gift Box*
ARTIST:
Russ Kramer

This detailed ceramic relief stein is the third in the Busch Gardens series that honors the theme park's efforts to preserve our environment. An exceptional wildlife illustration depicts the many different types of animals living throughout Busch Gardens. The first lidded stein in the series, it also features a painted white tiger on a ceramic inlay in a pewter lid.

Sports Steins

This section's offerings focus on sporting events and famous athletes. From the excitement of fast-paced games like basketball and ice hockey to the American favorites of baseball and football, collectors have their choice of sports-related steins. Famous names like NASCAR driver Bill Elliott, baseball great Babe Ruth and Olympic medal winner Jim Thorpe are also individually featured on these detailed collectibles. ∿

Sports Steins

Contents of This Section

SIDE VIEW

DETAIL

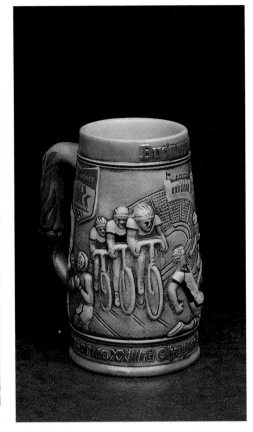

ISSUE YEAR:
1984
EDITION QUANTITY:
Not Available
ITEM NUMBER:
CS60

1984 Budweiser Olympic Games

HEIGHT:
6½"
ORIGIN:
Brazil
MANUFACTURER:
Ceramarte
MATERIAL:
Ceramic
SPECIAL FEATURE:
Bottom Stamp

Budweiser commemorates the 1984 Summer Olympics held in Los Angeles, California. The full relief stein depicts the Olympic events of boxing, cycling and track and field. The detailed handle resembles the flame of the Olympic torch.

SIDE VIEW

DETAIL

1988 Winter Olympic Games

Lidded

ISSUE YEAR:
1987
EDITION QUANTITY:
22,000
ITEM NUMBER:
CS81

This lidded stein pays tribute to the 1988 Winter Olympic Games hosted by Calgary, Canada. The vivid artwork depicts exciting Olympic events such as skiing, speed skating and ice hockey. The detailed band at top features shields from participating counties.

HEIGHT:
8½″
ORIGIN:
Gerz
MANUFACTURER:
Germany
MATERIAL:
Ceramic
LID:
Pewter
SPECIAL FEATURES:
Individually Numbered
Certificate of Authenticity
Bottom Stamp
Gift Box

SIDE VIEW

DETAIL

ISSUE YEAR:
1988
EDITION QUANTITY:
Not Available
ITEM NUMBER:
CS85

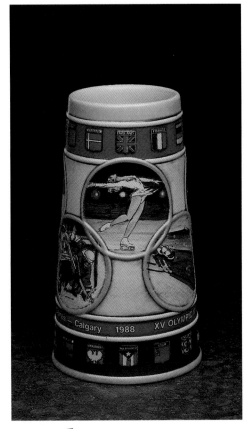

Budweiser Winter Olympic Games

HEIGHT:
7½″
ORIGIN:
Brazil
MANUFACTURER:
Ceramarte
MATERIAL:
Ceramic
SPECIAL FEATURES:
Bottom Stamp
Gift Box

This commemorative stein honors the athletes competing in the 1988 Winter Olympics in Calgary, Canada. The relief stein depicts Olympic events including skiing, figure skating and ski jumping. The red band at top and the blue band at bottom are decorated with shields from many of the countries that participated in the events.

SIDE VIEW

DETAIL

Bud Summer Olympic Games

Lidded

ISSUE YEAR:
1988
EDITION QUANTITY:
55,000
ITEM NUMBER:
CS91

This commemorative stein honors the athletes competing in the 1988 Summer Olympics in Seoul, South Korea. The relief stein depicts Olympic events including swimming, boxing and track and field. The blue band at bottom is decorated with shields from many of the countries that participated in the events. This stein also features a pewter lid with thumbrest.

HEIGHT:
8½"
ORIGIN:
Brazil
MANUFACTURER:
Ceramarte
MATERIAL:
Ceramic
LID:
Pewter
SPECIAL FEATURES:
Individually Numbered
Bottom Stamp
Gift Box

SIDE VIEW

DETAIL

ISSUE YEAR:
1988
EDITION QUANTITY:
Not Available
ITEM NUMBER:
CS92

Budweiser Summer Olympic Games

HEIGHT:
7½"
ORIGIN:
Brazil
MANUFACTURER:
Ceramarte
MATERIAL:
Ceramic

This stein honors the athletes competing in the 1988 Summer Olympics held in Seoul, South Korea. The illustrations, framed in Olympic rings, depict events including soccer, cycling, swimming, gymnastics and track and field. The red band at top and the blue band at bottom feature shields from countries participating in the games.

1992 U.S. Olympic Team Series

SIDE VIEW

DETAIL

'92 U.S. Olympic Winter Team

Lidded

ISSUE YEAR:
1991
EDITION QUANTITY:
25,000
ITEM NUMBER:
CS162
SERIES ORDER:
First

A full relief design, this stein pays tribute to the 1992 Winter Olympics held in Albertville, France. The colorful illustration details such events as figure skating, skiing, ice hockey and bobsledding. The 9″ stein features an Olympic Flame thumbrest and USA/five-ring logo on the pewter lid.

HEIGHT:
9″
ORIGIN:
Germany
MANUFACTURER:
Gerz
MATERIAL:
Ceramic
LID:
Pewter
SPECIAL FEATURES:
Individually Numbered
Certificate of Authenticity
Bottom Stamp
Gift Box
ARTIST:
Marcy Wilson

Anheuser-Busch is an official USOC Licensee: 36USC380

1992 U.S. Olympic Team Series

SIDE VIEW

DETAIL

'92 U.S. Olympic Summer Team

Lidded

ISSUE YEAR:
1992
EDITION QUANTITY:
25,000
ITEM NUMBER:
CS163
SERIES ORDER:
Second

HEIGHT:
9″
ORIGIN:
Germany
MANUFACTURER:
Gerz
MATERIAL:
Ceramic
LID:
Pewter
SPECIAL FEATURES:
Individually Numbered
Certificate of Authenticity
Bottom Stamp
Gift Box
ARTIST:
Marcy Wilson

This stein celebrates the sportsmanship at the 1992 Summer Olympics held in Barcelona, Spain. Six events are detailed in full relief including baseball, basketball, gymnastics, track, diving and equestrian. The 9″ stein features an Olympic Flame thumbrest and USA/five-ring logo on the pewter lid.

Anheuser-Busch is an official USOC Licensee: 36USC380

SIDE VIEW

DETAIL

Budweiser 1992 U.S. Olympic Team

ISSUE YEAR:
1991
EDITION QUANTITY:
50,000
ITEM NUMBER:
CS168

This lavishly illustrated stein depicts such Olympic events as basketball, figure skating, skiing and swimming. Manufactured in relief, international flags and the Budweiser Olympic logo frame each sport vignette. The USA/five-ring logo accents the handle. Sold individually and also packaged twelve-per case in a self-contained display bin.

HEIGHT:
5½"
ORIGIN:
Brazil
MANUFACTURER:
Ceramarte
MATERIAL:
Ceramic
SPECIAL FEATURES:
Individually Numbered Bottom Stamp
ARTIST:
Marcy Wilson

Anheuser-Busch is an official USOC Licensee: 36USC380

SIDE VIEW

DETAIL

ISSUE YEAR:
1995
EDITION QUANTITY:
Production limited
7/95 - 12/96
ITEM NUMBER:
CS259

HEIGHT:
8"
ORIGIN:
Brazil
MANUFACTURER:
Ceramarte
MATERIAL:
Ceramic
LID:
Pewter with
Ceramic Inlay
SPECIAL FEATURES:
Individually Numbered
Certificate of Authenticity
Bottom Stamp
Gift Box

Official Centennial Olympic Games
Lidded

The official Centennial Olympic Games Mark of Atlanta 1996 is featured in full-color relief on the front of this stein, and as a ceramic inlay in the solid pewter lid. The 8" tall stein is also distinguished by the official logos of previous Olympic venues in detailed relief. Top and bottom bands feature the centennial motif in green with gold accents and the centennial dates 1896 and 1996.

213

SIDE VIEW

DETAIL

Centennial Olympic Games Giftware

ISSUE YEAR:
1995
EDITION QUANTITY:
Open
ITEM NUMBER:
CS266

This deep relief stein features the official Centennial Olympic Games Mark of Atlanta 1996 in full color on the front. Each side depicts an ancient Greek athlete—a discus thrower and marathon runner. A classic Greek column forms the handle.

HEIGHT:
5¾"
ORIGIN:
Brazil
MANUFACTURER:
Ceramarte
MATERIAL:
Ceramic
SPECIAL FEATURES:
Certificate of Authenticity
Bottom Stamp
Gift Box

1996 U.S. Olympic Team Series

SIDE VIEW

DETAIL

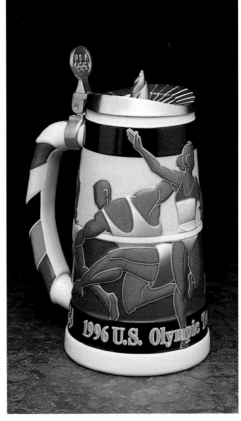

ISSUE YEAR:
1995
EDITION QUANTITY:
10,000
ITEM NUMBER:
CS246
SERIES ORDER:
First

1996 U.S. Olympic Team Track & Field
Lidded

HEIGHT:
8½"
ORIGIN:
Brazil
MANUFACTURER:
Ceramarte
MATERIAL:
Ceramic
LID:
Pewter
SPECIAL FEATURES:
Individually Numbered
Certificate of Authenticity
Bottom Stamp
Gift Box

A tribute to the track and field athletes of the 1996 U.S. Olympic Team, this 8½" tall ceramic relief stein features unique, stylized artwork of athletes in action. Part of the Anheuser-Busch Centennial U.S. Olympic Team Collection, the stein is topped by a solid pewter lid in the shape of an outdoor stadium.

Anheuser-Busch is an official USOC Licensee: 36USC380

1996 U.S. Olympic Team Series

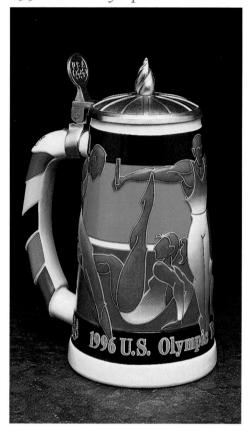

SIDE VIEW

DETAIL

1996 U.S. Olympic Team Gymnastics

Lidded

ISSUE YEAR:
1995
EDITION QUANTITY:
10,000
ITEM NUMBER:
CS262
SERIES ORDER:
Second

From the Anheuser-Busch Centennial U.S. Olympic Team Collection, this 8½" tall stein salutes the gymnasts of the 1996 U.S. Olympic Team. Stylized artwork of gymnastics competitors appears in detailed ceramic relief. The distinctive solid pewter lid is in the shape of an indoor stadium.

HEIGHT:
8½"
ORIGIN:
Brazil
MANUFACTURER:
Ceramarte
MATERIAL:
Ceramic
LID:
Pewter
SPECIAL FEATURES:
Individually Numbered
Certificate of Authenticity
Bottom Stamp
Gift Box

Anheuser-Busch is an official USOC Licensee: 36USC380

SIDE VIEW

DETAIL

ISSUE YEAR:
1996
EDITION QUANTITY:
Open
ITEM NUMBER:
CS249

Budweiser Atlanta 1996 Olympic Games

HEIGHT:
5¾″
ORIGIN:
Brazil
MANUFACTURER:
Ceramarte
MATERIAL:
Ceramic
SPECIAL FEATURES:
Certificate of Authenticity
Bottom Stamp
Gift Box

To commemorate the Centennial Olympic Games, this detailed relief stein showcases the sites of both the 1896 and 1996 Games. One side features Athens and its magnificent Parthenon. On the other side is the skyline of Atlanta. In the center is the official Centennial Olympic Games Mark of Atlanta 1996. A replica of the Olympic flame sits atop the handle.

SIDE VIEW

DETAIL

Centennial Olympic Games Premier Edition
Lidded

This unique stein is 22" tall and 5" in diameter. The front is highlighted by a full-relief, hand-painted depiction of the Atlanta 1996 Centennial Olympic Games Collection Logo. The sides and top bottom bands feature detailed relief engravings of the official Olympic pictograms. An Olympic flame replica tops the large square lid and a vine-covered column forms the handle.

ISSUE YEAR:
1996
EDITION QUANTITY:
1,996
ITEM NUMBER:
CS267

HEIGHT:
22"
ORIGIN:
Germany
MANUFACTURER:
Gerz
MATERIAL:
Ceramic
LID:
Ceramic
SPECIAL FEATURES:
Individually Numbered
Certificate of Authenticity
Bottom Stamp
Gift Box

Sports History Series

SIDE VIEW

DETAIL

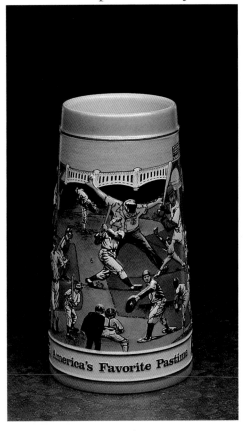

ISSUE YEAR:
1990
EDITION QUANTITY:
100,000
ITEM NUMBER:
CS124
SERIES ORDER:
First

America's Favorite Pastime

HEIGHT:
7½″
ORIGIN:
Brazil
MANUFACTURER:
Ceramarte
MATERIAL:
Ceramic
SPECIAL FEATURES:
Individually Numbered
Certificate of Authenticity
Bottom Stamp
Gift Box
ARTIST:
Mike Weaver

B aseball's colorful history is traced on this relief ceramic stein, first in the Sports History series. America's Favorite Pastime recalls the evolution of baseball from the early 1900s to present day and sports a unique handle to form a modern-day baseball bat and ball.

Sports History Series

SIDE VIEW

DETAIL

Gridiron Legacy

ISSUE YEAR:
1991
EDITION QUANTITY:
100,000
ITEM NUMBER:
CS128
SERIES ORDER:
Second

The history of football is remembered on this full relief ceramic stein, the second in the Sports History stein series. Gridiron Legacy traces the sport from its beginnings to the modern format around this colorfully illustrated stein. A unique handle is shaped to resemble a goal post.

HEIGHT:
7½″
ORIGIN:
Brazil
MANUFACTURER:
Ceramarte
MATERIAL:
Ceramic
SPECIAL FEATURES:
Individually Numbered
Certificate of Authenticity
Bottom Stamp
Gift Box
ARTIST:
Mike Weaver

Sports History Series

SIDE VIEW

DETAIL

ISSUE YEAR:
1991
EDITION QUANTITY:
100,000
ITEM NUMBER:
CS132
SERIES ORDER:
Third

Chasing The Checkered Flag

HEIGHT:
7½"
ORIGIN:
Brazil
MANUFACTURER:
Ceramarte
MATERIAL:
Ceramic
SPECIAL FEATURES:
Individually Numbered
Certificate of Authenticity
Bottom Stamp
Gift Box
ARTIST:
Mike Weaver

The third in the Sports series, Chasing The Checkered Flag pays tribute to the exciting sport of auto racing. The colorful illustration depicts the history of the sport from the dirt tracks and pre-World War I production models to the modern asphalt tracks and grand prix race cars of today. To accent the design, the unique handle resembles a gear shift.

Sports History Series

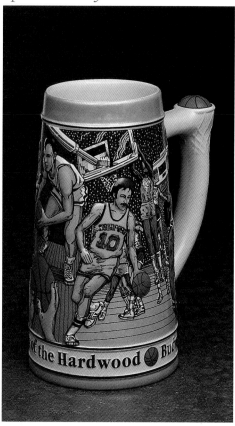

SIDE VIEW

DETAIL

Heroes Of The Hardwood

ISSUE YEAR:
1991
EDITION QUANTITY:
100,000
ITEM NUMBER:
CS134
SERIES ORDER:
Fourth

Basketball's fast-paced history is depicted on Heroes Of The Hardwood, the fourth stein in the Sports series. The detailed illustration recounts the game's simple beginnings to the hard-driving game of today. To accent the design, the unique handle resembles a basketball and hoop.

HEIGHT:
7½″
ORIGIN:
Brazil
MANUFACTURER:
Ceramarte
MATERIAL:
Ceramic
SPECIAL FEATURES:
Individually Numbered
Certificate of Authenticity
Bottom Stamp
Gift Box
ARTIST:
Mike Weaver

SIDE VIEW

DETAIL

ISSUE YEAR:
1992
EDITION QUANTITY:
100,000
ITEM NUMBER:
CS165
SERIES ORDER:
Fifth

Par For The Course

HEIGHT:
7½"
ORIGIN:
Brazil
MANUFACTURER:
Ceramarte
MATERIAL:
Ceramic
SPECIAL FEATURES:
Individually Numbered
Certificate of Authenticity
Bottom Stamp
Gift Box
ARTIST:
Paul Radke

Par For The Course, the fifth addition to the Sport series, honors the 500-year-old sport of golf. The colorful illustration traces the history of the ancient game and highlights changes in fashion and equipment. To accent the design, the unique handle resembles a golf club grip.

Sports History Series

SIDE VIEW

DETAIL

Center Ice

ISSUE YEAR:
1993
EDITION QUANTITY:
100,000
ITEM NUMBER:
CS209
SERIES ORDER:
Sixth & Final

The sixth stein in the Sports History series, Center Ice details the distinctive heritage of ice hockey. The detailed relief captures the thrill of the game from its beginnings in the 1860s to the professional teams of today. With scenes of skating, slap shots and scoring, this colorful edition is accented with a handle which resembles a hockey stick.

HEIGHT:
7½"
ORIGIN:
Brazil
MANUFACTURER:
Ceramarte
MATERIAL:
Ceramic
SPECIAL FEATURES:
Individually Numbered
Certificate of Authenticity
Bottom Stamp
Gift Box
ARTIST:
Paul Radke

SIDE VIEW

DETAIL

ISSUE YEAR:
1991
EDITION QUANTITY:
50,000
ITEM NUMBER:
CS142
SERIES ORDER:
First

Babe Ruth

Lidded

HEIGHT:
9″
ORIGIN:
Germany
MANUFACTURER:
Gerz
MATERIAL:
Ceramic
LID:
Pewter
SPECIAL FEATURES:
Individually Numbered
Certificate of Authenticity
Bottom Stamp
Gift Box
ARTIST:
Mike Caito

The first stein in the Sports Legends series honors Babe Ruth, the most remembered player in the history of baseball. The striking illustration depicts the Babe's legendary home run in 1932 at Chicago's Wrigley Field. A pewter lid with a stylized baseball thumbrest tops the stein.

©*1993 Curtis Publishing Company.*

Sports Legends Series

SIDE VIEW

DETAIL

Jim Thorpe

Lidded

ISSUE YEAR:
1992
EDITION QUANTITY:
50,000
ITEM NUMBER:
CS171
SERIES ORDER:
Second

Jim Thorpe, considered to be one of the finest athletes in American history, is remembered on the second stein in the Sports Legends series. The illustration highlights this athlete's impressive accomplishments from his legendary Olympic achievements to his years playing football. The pewter lid is detailed with a football-shaped thumbrest.

HEIGHT:
9″
ORIGIN:
Germany
MANUFACTURER:
Gerz
MATERIAL:
Ceramic
LID:
Pewter
SPECIAL FEATURES:
Individually Numbered
Certificate of Authenticity
Bottom Stamp
Gift Box
ARTIST:
Mike Caito

Sports Legends Series

SIDE VIEW

DETAIL

ISSUE YEAR:
1993
EDITION QUANTITY:
50,000
ITEM NUMBER:
CS206
SERIES ORDER:
Third & Final

Joe Louis

Lidded

HEIGHT:
9″
ORIGIN:
Germany
MANUFACTURER:
Gerz
MATERIAL:
Ceramic
LID:
Pewter
SPECIAL FEATURES:
Individually Numbered
Certificate of Authenticity
Bottom Stamp
Gift Box
ARTIST:
Mike Caito

The Joe Louis stein pays tribute to this incredible athlete who held the heavyweight championship for twelve years (1937-49), the longest in boxing history. This hand-crafted stein, bordered with detail relief, honors the champion as he will be remembered: in the ring. The pewter thumbrest resembles boxing gloves.

©1993 Curtis Publishing Company.

SIDE VIEW

DETAIL

Racing Team

ISSUE YEAR:
1993
EDITION QUANTITY:
Open
ITEM NUMBER:
CS194
SERIES ORDER:
Second

Second in the Budweiser Racing series, this ceramic stein pays tribute to the winning team of manager Junior Johnson and driver Bill Elliott. Both are captured in raceway excitement. Junior and Bill have added their signatures beneath their portraits. Bold graphics and colors evoke the thrill of the race with black and white checkered flags and the Bud race car.

HEIGHT:
6″
ORIGIN:
Brazil
MANUFACTURER:
Ceramarte
MATERIAL:
Ceramic
SPECIAL FEATURES:
Certificate of Authenticity
Bottom Stamp
Gift Box
ARTIST:
Hans Droog

SIDE VIEW

DETAIL

Bill Elliott

ISSUE YEAR:
1993
ITEM NUMBER/
EDITION QUANTITY:
CS196: 25,000
CS196SE: 1,500*

Lidded

HEIGHT:
10½″
ORIGIN:
Germany
MANUFACTURER:
Gerz
MATERIAL:
Ceramic
LID:
Pewter
SPECIAL FEATURES:
Individually Numbered
Certificate of Authenticity
Bottom Stamp
Gift Box
Driver's Signature
ARTIST:
Hans Droog

The Bill Elliott stein honors one of stock car racing's most popular and successful drivers. He is shown roaring to victory against an exciting racing background and the traditional checkered flags. The solid pewter lid holds a detailed figurine of the Budweiser NASCAR #11 on top.

* *CS196SE: Each stein in the 1,500 piece signature edition was personally signed by Bill Elliott.*

SIDE VIEW

DETAIL

Official 1994 World Cup Commemorative

Lidded

ISSUE YEAR:
1994
EDITION QUANTITY:
25,000
ITEM NUMBER:
CS230

This stein was commissioned to commemorate the 1994 World Cup, played in the United States. The ceramic relief stein features an action illustration of the world's most popular sport, along with the official World Cup logo. A list of each U.S. host city and the dates of play appear in a bottom band. The unique solid pewter lid features a ceramic soccer ball and a soccer shoe thumbrest.

HEIGHT:
8¾"
ORIGIN:
Brazil
MANUFACTURER:
Ceramarte
MATERIAL:
Ceramic
LID:
Pewter with Ceramic Figurine
SPECIAL FEATURES:
Individually Numbered Certificate of Authenticity Bottom Stamp Gift Box
ARTIST:
Jeff Tull

Notes

Anheuser-Busch Collectors Club Steins

As the recognized leader in collectible beer steins, it seemed natural for Anheuser-Busch to begin a national club devoted to stein collectors. Introduced in 1995, the Anheuser-Busch Collectors Club was an immediate success. The steins in this section are all exclusive issues that were available only to club members. Each year, members receive a new Membership Stein as a part of their club membership. In addition, they have the option to purchase Members Only Steins in the years in which they are members. ∽

Anheuser-Busch Collectors Club Steins

Contents of This Section

Membership Stein Series

SIDE VIEW

DETAIL

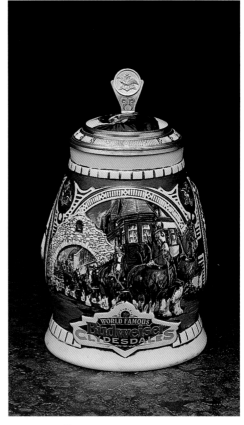

ISSUE YEAR:
1995

EDITION QUANTITY:
*Limited to 1995
Club Membership*

ITEM NUMBER:
CB1

SERIES ORDER:
First

Budweiser Clydesdales at the Bauernhof
Lidded

HEIGHT:
7½″

ORIGIN:
Brazil

MANUFACTURER:
Ceramarte

MATERIAL:
Ceramic

LID:
*Pewter with
Ceramic Inlay*

SPECIAL FEATURES:
*Individually Numbered
Certificate of Authenticity
Bottom Stamp
Gift Box*

ARTIST:
Anthony Leon

The Collectors Club Charter Year Membership Stein features the Budweiser Clydesdale hitch as it storms out of the Bauernhof Courtyard at Grant's Farm in St. Louis. Two oval vignettes depict a Clydesdale head in full harness and a traditional beer wagon dalmatian. Produced in detailed relief, with ceramic-inlay pewter lid. Handle resembles a leather strap.

Members Only Stein Series

SIDE VIEW

DETAIL

The Brew House Clock Tower

Lidded

ISSUE YEAR:
1995

EDITION QUANTITY:
*Available to 1995
Club Members Only*

ITEM NUMBER:
CB2

SERIES ORDER:
First

The Collectors Club Charter Year Members Only Stein replicates the famous Anheuser-Busch Brew House, a National Historic Landmark built in St. Louis in 1892. The 9½" tall rectangular stein features intricate relief work throughout. The lid includes the first working clock ever set in an Anheuser-Busch stein. Unique column-style handle is topped with a pewter thumb rest.

HEIGHT:
9½"

ORIGIN:
Brazil

MANUFACTURER:
Ceramarte

MATERIAL:
Ceramic

LID:
Ceramic

SPECIAL FEATURES:
*Working Quartz Clock
Individually Numbered
Certificate of Authenticity
Bottom Stamp
Gift Box*

ARTIST:
Doug Thompson

Membership Stein Series

SIDE VIEW

DETAIL

ISSUE YEAR:
1996

EDITION QUANTITY:
*Limited to 1996
Club Membership*

ITEM NUMBER:
CS3

SERIES ORDER:
Second

HEIGHT:
7″

ORIGIN:
Brazil

MANUFACTURER:
Ceramarte

MATERIAL:
Ceramic

LID:
*Pewter with
Ceramic Inlay*

SPECIAL FEATURES:
*Individually Numbered
Certificate of Authenticity
Bottom Stamp
Gift Box*

ARTIST:
Anthony Leon

World's Largest Brewer

Lidded

Issued only to 1996 members, this second Anheuser-Busch Collectors Club Membership Stein features several images from the late 1800s. Against a backdrop of an old-world map, the stein highlights a vintage 1890 A&Eagle logo centered between two historic Anheuser-Busch buildings: the Brew House and the Old School House. The words "World's Largest Brewer" appear at the bottom.

Members Only Stein Series

SIDE VIEW

DETAIL

King— A Regal Spirit

Lidded

ISSUE YEAR:
1996
EDITION QUANTITY:
Available to 1996 Club Members Only
ITEM NUMBER:
CB4
SERIES ORDER:
Second

The second Collectors Club Members Only Stein is a detailed reproduction of a Clydesdale head in full harness gear. "King—A Regal Spirit" is named for an actual Clydesdale used in one of the Budweiser eight-horse performing hitches. The stein is extremely authentic in every detail, down to the black blinders with A&Eagle logos worn by Clydesdales while on the hitch.

HEIGHT:
9˝
ORIGIN:
Brazil
MANUFACTURER:
Ceramarte
MATERIAL:
Ceramic
LID:
Ceramic
SPECIAL FEATURES:
*Individually Numbered
Certificate of Authenticity
Bottom Stamp
Gift Box*
ARTIST:
Doug Thompson

Notes

Gerz Meisterwerke & Collectorwerke

In keeping with the Anheuser-Busch commitment to quality and long-standing tradition of excellence, a collaboration was formed with S.P. Gerz Company of Sessenbach, Germany. The Anheuser-Busch exacting standards combined with the Gerz centuries of experience have resulted in these exquisitely crafted, limited edition steins. ❧

Gerz Meisterwerke & Collectorwerke

Contents of This Section

"Saturday Evening Post" Christmas Collection

SIDE VIEW

DETAIL

ISSUE YEAR:
1992

EDITION QUANTITY:
5,000

ITEM NUMBER:
GM1

SERIES ORDER:
First

Santa's Mailbag

Lidded

HEIGHT:
10¾"

ORIGIN:
Germany

MANUFACTURER:
Gerz

MATERIAL:
Ceramic

LID:
Pewter

SPECIAL FEATURES:
Individually Numbered
Certificate of Authenticity
Handpainted
Bottom Stamp
Gift Box

This is the first in a series of ceramic relief steins inspired by magazine covers from *The Saturday Evening Post.* This limited edition stein features artwork from a Norman Rockwell illustration which first appeared in The Post on December 21, 1935. Because each stein is handpainted, no two are exactly alike, making each one a unique masterpiece.

©*1993 Curtis Publishing Co.*

"Saturday Evening Post" Christmas Collection

SIDE VIEW

DETAIL

Santa's Helper

Lidded

ISSUE YEAR:
1993
EDITION QUANTITY:
7,500
ITEM NUMBER:
GM3
SERIES ORDER:
Second

For over 40 years, J.C. Leyendecker contributed 322 cover illustrations to the *The Saturday Evening Post.* One of his finest works, the December 20, 1930, cover has been crafted in exquisite detail. This handpainted stein is topped with a solid pewter lid stacked with holiday packages.

HEIGHT:
10½"
ORIGIN:
Germany
MANUFACTURER:
Gerz
MATERIAL:
Ceramic
LID:
Pewter
SPECIAL FEATURES:
Individually Numbered
Certificate of Authenticity
Handpainted
Bottom Stamp
Gift Box
Modeler's Initials
Engraved on Stein

©1993 Curtis Publishing Co.

"Saturday Evening Post" Christmas Collection

SIDE VIEW

DETAIL

ISSUE YEAR:
1994

EDITION QUANTITY:
5,000

ITEM NUMBER:
GM13

SERIES ORDER:
Third

All I Want For Christmas

Lidded

HEIGHT:
10⅞"

ORIGIN:
Germany

MANUFACTURER:
Gerz

MATERIAL:
Ceramic

LID:
Pewter

SPECIAL FEATURES:
Individually Numbered
Handpainted
Bottom Stamp
Gift Box

This is the third stein in the nostalgic series featuring magazine covers from the *Saturday Evening Post*. Originally published on December 22, 1923, this outstanding cover illustration by noted artist J.C. Leyendecker has been beautifully reproduced in deep relief. The stein's solid pewter lid is detailed in a holly motif and is topped with a star rising above the clouds.

First Hunt Series

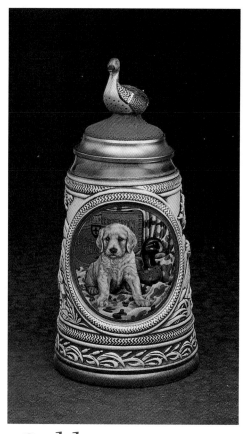

SIDE VIEW

DETAIL

Golden Retriever

Lidded

ISSUE YEAR:
1993
EDITION QUANTITY:
10,000
ITEM NUMBER:
GM2
SERIES ORDER:
First

The splendor and exhilaration of the first hunt is captured in this limited edition stein series. The first of four steins, Golden Retriever captures the rough beauty and natural allure of the outdoors in fine ceramic relief. The stein handle is fashioned after a leather dog collar; the lid has a pewter rim with ceramic duck figurine on top.

HEIGHT:
10″
ORIGIN:
Germany
MANUFACTURER:
Gerz
MATERIAL:
Ceramic
LID:
Pewter with Ceramic Figurine
SPECIAL FEATURES:
Individually Numbered Certificate of Authenticity Bottom Stamp Gift Box
ARTIST:
Pat Ford

First Hunt Series

SIDE VIEW

DETAIL

Springer Spaniel

Lidded

ISSUE YEAR:
1994

EDITION QUANTITY:
10,000

ITEM NUMBER:
GM5

SERIES ORDER:
Second

HEIGHT:
10″

ORIGIN:
Germany

MANUFACTURER:
Gerz

MATERIAL:
Ceramic

LID:
Pewter with Ceramic Figurine

SPECIAL FEATURES:
Individually Numbered Bottom Stamp
Gift Box

ARTIST:
Pat Ford

Second in the First Hunt Series, this stein showcases an impressive, full-color illustration of a springer spaniel puppy awaiting the day of his first hunt. A ceramic duck figurine tops the lid, which also has an acorn thumbrest. The handle is shaped like a leather dog collar and holds the stein's individually numbered "dog tag."

First Hunt Series

SIDE VIEW

DETAIL

Pointer

Lidded

ISSUE YEAR:
1995
EDITION QUANTITY:
10,000
ITEM NUMBER:
GM16
SERIES ORDER:
Third

The third edition in the First Hunt Series depicts the pointer puppy with traditional spotted markings and pointed tail. The detailed pewter lid features a ceramic quail figurine and a pewter thumbrest in the shape of two acorns. Each stein is uniquely numbered on a "dog tag" which hangs around the collar-shaped handle.

HEIGHT:
10″
ORIGIN:
Germany
MANUFACTURER:
Gerz
MATERIAL:
Ceramic
LID:
Pewter with Ceramic Figurine
SPECIAL FEATURES:
*Individually Numbered Bottom Stamp
Gift Box*
ARTIST:
Pat Ford

First Hunt Series

SIDE VIEW

DETAIL

ISSUE YEAR:
1996
EDITION QUANTITY:
10,000
ITEM NUMBER:
GM17
SERIES ORDER:
Fourth

Labrador

Lidded

HEIGHT:
10˝
ORIGIN:
Germany
MANUFACTURER:
Gerz
MATERIAL:
Ceramic
LID:
*Pewter with
Ceramic Figurine*
SPECIAL FEATURES:
*Individually Numbered
Bottom Stamp
Gift Box*
ARTIST:
Pat Ford

The First Hunt Series closes with this fourth and final stein, featuring a detailed illustration of a Labrador puppy. In keeping with the others in the series, this stein includes a pewter lid with a hand-painted ceramic duck figurine and an acorn thumbrest. The handle is in the shape of a leather dog collar. Steins are individually numbered on the handle's "dog tag."

American Heritage Collection

SIDE VIEW

DETAIL

John F. Kennedy

Lidded

ISSUE YEAR:
1993
EDITION QUANTITY:
10,000
ITEM NUMBER:
GM4
SERIES ORDER:
First

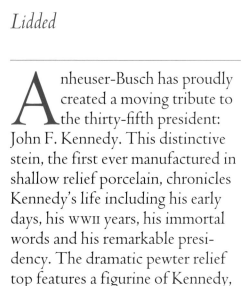

Anheuser-Busch has proudly created a moving tribute to the thirty-fifth president: John F. Kennedy. This distinctive stein, the first ever manufactured in shallow relief porcelain, chronicles Kennedy's life including his early days, his WWII years, his immortal words and his remarkable presidency. The dramatic pewter relief top features a figurine of Kennedy, capturing the spirit of Camelot.

HEIGHT:
12″
ORIGIN:
Germany
MANUFACTURER:
Gerz
MATERIAL:
Porcelain
LID:
Pewter
SPECIAL FEATURES:
Individually Numbered
Certificate of Authenticity
Bottom Stamp
Gift Box
ARTIST:
Don Langeneckert

SIDE VIEW

DETAIL

ISSUE YEAR:
1994
EDITION QUANTITY:
5,000
ITEM NUMBER:
GM6

Triple Self-Portrait

Lidded

HEIGHT:
12¼″
ORIGIN:
Germany
MANUFACTURER:
Gerz
MATERIAL:
Porcelain
LID:
Pewter
SPECIAL FEATURES:
Lithophane Base
Mirror-Like Inset in
Figurine on Lid
Individually Numbered
Gift Box

In honor of the centennial of Norman Rockwell's birth, this white porcelain stein presents three views of his famous painting, "Triple Self-Portrait." The first is the large full-color depiction on the stein body. The second is a detailed, solid pewter, sculptured lid with reflective mirror-like inset. The third view can only be seen by looking through the stein while holding the base up to the light.

SIDE VIEW

DETAIL

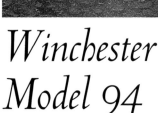

Winchester Model 94

Lidded

ISSUE YEAR:
1994
EDITION QUANTITY:
5,000
ITEM NUMBER:
GM10

This deep relief ceramic stein celebrates 100 years of continuous production of the Winchester Model 94, the most famous lever-action rifle of all time. Historic western artwork from the Winchester archives is brilliantly reproduced in full-color relief. The intricately-detailed pewter lid is topped with a figurine of the signature Winchester horse and rider.

HEIGHT:
9"
ORIGIN:
Germany
MANUFACTURER:
Gerz
MATERIAL:
Ceramic
LID:
Pewter
SPECIAL FEATURES:
Individually Numbered
Bottom Stamp
Gift Box

SIDE VIEW

DETAIL

ISSUE YEAR:
1995
EDITION QUANTITY:
5,000
ITEM NUMBER:
GM9

Rosie the Riveter

Lidded

HEIGHT:
11″
ORIGIN:
Germany
MANUFACTURER:
Gerz
MATERIAL:
Ceramic
LID:
Pewter
SPECIAL FEATURES:
Individually Numbered
Bottom Stamp
Gift Box

Reproduced on this patriotic stein is Norman Rockwell's May 29th, 1943 cover illustration for *The Saturday Evening Post*—a tribute to all women who answered the wartime call to keep America's factories working. The detailed pewter lid displays the words "Portrait of America" and is topped with a figurine of Rockwell's easel holding a painting of a proud eagle's head.

253

SIDE VIEW

DETAIL

Mallard

Lidded

ISSUE YEAR:
1994
EDITION QUANTITY:
5,000
ITEM NUMBER:
GM7

Another impressive creation from the artisans of Gerz Meisterwerke, this full-dimensional, deep relief ceramic stein features the richly colored mallard duck in its natural environment. The size of the stein is truly unique at 7¾"tall and 10"deep. The solid pewter lid includes a ceramic inlay.

HEIGHT:
7¾"
ORIGIN:
Germany
MANUFACTURER:
Gerz
MATERIAL:
Ceramic
LID:
Pewter with Ceramic Inlay
SPECIAL FEATURES:
Individually Numbered
Handpainted
Bottom Stamp
Gift Box

SIDE VIEW

DETAIL

ISSUE YEAR:
1995
EDITION QUANTITY:
3,500
ITEM NUMBER:
GM8

Giant Panda

Lidded

HEIGHT:
9¼"
ORIGIN:
Germany
MANUFACTURER:
Gerz
MATERIAL:
Ceramic
LID:
*Pewter with
Ceramic Inlay*
SPECIAL FEATURES:
*Individually Numbered
Handpainted
Bottom Stamp
Gift Box*

From the artisans of Gerz Meisterwerke, this truly distinctive stein features full three-dimensional modeling, deep relief design and handpainted detailing. A playful giant panda seems to be reaching out of the front of the stein, while a panda cub appears on the side. The stein stands 9¼" tall and is 8¼" deep. The solid pewter lid has a ceramic inlay.

Favorite Pastimes

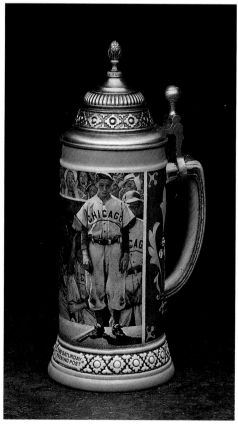

SIDE VIEW

DETAIL

The Dugout

ISSUE YEAR:
1993
EDITION QUANTITY:
10,000
ITEM NUMBER:
GL1
SERIES ORDER:
First

Lidded

This remarkable stein immortalizes a vintage *Saturday Evening Post* illustration by American legend Norman Rockwell. The Dugout, expertly crafted in full relief, is a humorous study of one very frustrated baseball team. This richly designed stein is enhanced with a detailed pewter lid and baseball thumbrest.

HEIGHT:
10½″
ORIGIN:
Germany
MANUFACTURER:
Gerz
MATERIAL:
Ceramic
LID:
Pewter
SPECIAL FEATURES:
Individually Numbered
Certificate of Authenticity
Bottom Stamp
Gift Box

SIDE VIEW

DETAIL

Winchester

Lidded

ISSUE YEAR:
1994
EDITION QUANTITY:
10,000
ITEM NUMBER:
GL2

HEIGHT:
7½"
ORIGIN:
Germany
MANUFACTURER:
Gerz
MATERIAL:
Ceramic
LID:
Pewter
SPECIAL FEATURES:
*Individually Numbered
Bottom Stamp
Gift Box*

The famous Winchester rifle, known as the "Gun That Won The West," is honored on this 7½" tall ceramic stein. The center panel displays the legendary Winchester logo in full color against a white background. The stein also features deep relief sides, a rope-shaped handle and base, and a detailed pewter lid with etched Winchester logo and saddle horn thumbrest.

"Saturday Evening Post" Christmas Collector Series

SIDE VIEW

DETAIL

"Saturday Evening Post" Christmas

ISSUE YEAR:
1995
EDITION QUANTITY:
5,000
ITEM NUMBER:
GL5
SERIES ORDER:
First

Renowned artist Norman Rockwell's 1926 cover illustration for the *Saturday Evening Post* is showcased on this first stein in the series. The shallow-relief ceramic stein is also decorated with traditional holly leaves and berries. The solid pewter lid features an embossed Christmas design and a unique Christmas tree thumbrest.

HEIGHT:
8″
ORIGIN:
Germany
MANUFACTURER:
Gerz
MATERIAL:
Ceramic
LID:
Pewter
SPECIAL FEATURES:
*Individually Numbered
Bottom Stamp
Gift Box*

Notes

Mission Hall
elville, New York

Dear Anheuser Bus

I found a stein rec
an antique store
I've enclosed a s
Please contact me
is helpful.

Sincerely,
Dan Peterson

USA

The Search Is On...

Although the information about the steins in this section is limited, names and item numbers have been listed for collectors. We continue to search for more information on this group of steins and encourage collectors and customers to contact Anheuser-Busch with any relevant information. Please send written correspondence to the address listed in the preface of this book. ☙

The Search Is On...

Contents of This Section

Mini Mug Set Of Four

ISSUE YEAR:
Not Available
EDITION QUANTITY:
Open
ITEM NUMBER:
CS8

HEIGHT:
2¼"
ORIGIN:
Brazil
MANUFACTURER:
Ceramarte
MATERIAL:
Ceramic

This set of mini mugs features label graphic decals of four of Anheuser-Busch's popular beer brands: Budweiser, Michelob, Busch and Natural Light. Each grey ceramic mini mug stands 2¼" high.

Clydesdales

ISSUE YEAR:
1976
EDITION QUANTITY:
Open
ITEM NUMBER:
CS12

HEIGHT:
6½"
ORIGIN:
USA
MANUFACTURER:
Unknown
MATERIAL:
Ceramic

This early edition features the World Famous Budweiser Clydesdales. The Clydesdales are shown in the traditional eight-horse hitch and encircles the attractive stein. A red A&Eagle symbol enhances the design. This is the unlidded version of CSL9.

Coracao Decanter Set

ISSUE YEAR:
1976
EDITION QUANTITY:
Open
ITEM NUMBER:
CS31

This seven piece set includes a decanter and six wine cups. The relief decanter features a German man and woman surrounded by a flower border. Three of the cups are decaled with female figures, the other three are decaled with male figures.

HEIGHT:
6½″ decanter
2½″ cups
ORIGIN:
Brazil
MANUFACTURER:
Ceramarte
MATERIAL:
Ceramic

Holanda Decanter Set

Antique Brown

ISSUE YEAR:
1976
EDITION QUANTITY:
Open
ITEM NUMBER:
CS34

The spirit of the Netherlands is recalled on this seven piece Holanda Decanter Set. The old world decanter and cups, crafted in antique brown, feature illustrated male and female figures. This uniquely designed set was also produced in cobalt blue.

HEIGHT:
Not Available
ORIGIN:
Brazil
MANUFACTURER:
Ceramarte
MATERIAL:
Ceramic

Holanda Decanter Set

Blue

ISSUE YEAR:
1976
EDITION QUANTITY:
Open
ITEM NUMBER:
CS35

HEIGHT:
Not Available
ORIGIN:
Brazil
MANUFACTURER:
Ceramarte
MATERIAL:
Ceramic

The spirit of the Netherlands is recalled on Anheuser-Busch's seven piece Holanda Decanter Set. The cobalt blue design on the decanter and cups, reminiscent of Holland's popular delft earthenware, feature illustrated male and female figures. This uniquely designed set was also produced in antique brown.

Canteen Decanter Set

Lidded

ISSUE YEAR:
1976
EDITION QUANTITY:
Open
ITEM NUMBER:
CS36

HEIGHT:
Not Available
ORIGIN:
Brazil
MANUFACTURER:
Ceramarte
MATERIAL:
Ceramic
LID:
Ceramic

This seven piece decanter set consists of one decanter with six cups. Made of ceramic, the set is earth brown and features a floral motif.

Natural Light

ISSUE YEAR:
1980
EDITION QUANTITY:
Open
ITEM NUMBER:
CS43

Hofbrau Style

This half-liter style, introduced in 1980, depicts the Anheuser-Busch Natural Light trademark.

HEIGHT:
5″
ORIGIN:
Brazil
MANUFACTURER:
Ceramarte
MATERIAL:
Ceramic

Busch

ISSUE YEAR:
1980
EDITION QUANTITY:
Open
ITEM NUMBER:
CS44

Hofbrau Style

Introduced in 1980, this ceramic stein prominently displays the distinctive Busch mountains graphics from the brand's label. The Hofbrau-style stein also features the Anheuser-Busch A&Eagle trademark.

HEIGHT:
5″
ORIGIN:
Brazil
MANUFACTURER:
Ceramarte
MATERIAL:
Ceramic

ISSUE YEAR:
1980
EDITION QUANTITY:
Open
ITEM NUMBER:
CS45

Michelob

Hofbrau Style

HEIGHT:
5″
ORIGIN:
Brazil
MANUFACTURER:
Ceramarte
MATERIAL:
Ceramic

The red and gold ribbons of the Michelob logo add to the attractive look of this Hofbrau style ceramic stein.

ISSUE YEAR:
1980
EDITION QUANTITY:
Open
ITEM NUMBER:
CS46

Budweiser

Hofbrau Style

HEIGHT:
5″
ORIGIN:
Brazil
MANUFACTURER:
Ceramarte
MATERIAL:
Ceramic

Budweiser, the world's largest selling brand of beer, is featured on this traditional Hofbrau style stein. The colorful Budweiser label graphics include the ribbon and medallion and the trademark A&Eagle.

Special Event Steins

nheuser-Busch has offered its wholesalers a number of steins created specifically for special promotional events. Although these steins were never intended to be available to the public, many collectors have purchased the steins over the years. The featured subjects include sporting events, city celebrations, annual festivals and regional wildlife themes. ∽

Special Event Steins

Contents of This Section

Special Event Steins

Contents of This Section (continued)

Budweiser
Chicago Skyline

ISSUE YEAR: *1980*
EDITION QUANTITY: *100,000*
ITEM NUMBER: *CS40*
HEIGHT: *7˝*
MANUFACTURER: *Ceramarte, Brazil*
SPECIAL FEATURE: *Bottom Stamp*

Budweiser
Chicagoland

ISSUE YEAR: *1981*
EDITION QUANTITY: *100,000*
ITEM NUMBER: *CS51*
HEIGHT: *7½˝*
MANUFACTURER: *Ceramarte, Brazil*
SPECIAL FEATURE: *Bottom Stamp*

Budweiser
Texas

ISSUE YEAR: *1981*
EDITION QUANTITY: *Not Available*
ITEM NUMBER: *CS52*
HEIGHT: *8˝*
MANUFACTURER: *Ceramarte, Brazil*
SPECIAL FEATURE: *Bottom Stamp*

Budweiser
California

ISSUE YEAR: *1981*
EDITION QUANTITY: *Not Available*
ITEM NUMBER: *CS56*
HEIGHT: *7½˝*
MANUFACTURER: *Ceramarte, Brazil*
SPECIAL FEATURE: *Bottom Stamp*

1983-90

Budweiser
San Francisco

ISSUE YEAR: *1983*
EDITION QUANTITY: *Not Available*
ITEM NUMBER: *CS59*
HEIGHT: *7½"*
MANUFACTURER: *Ceramarte, Brazil*
SPECIAL FEATURE: *Bottom Stamp*

North/South Dakota

ISSUE YEAR: *1989*
EDITION QUANTITY: *7,054*
ITEM NUMBER: *SO42268*
HEIGHT: *5¼"*
MANUFACTURER: *Gerz, West Germany*
Decorated in USA

California
Big Bear Oktoberfest
20th Anniversary

ISSUE YEAR: *1990*
EDITION QUANTITY: *504*
ITEM NUMBER: *SO49433*
HEIGHT: *5¼"*
MANUFACTURER: *Gerz, West Germany*
Decorated in USA
SPECIAL FEATURE: *Individually Numbered*

Daytona
Bud Bike Week

ISSUE YEAR: *1990*
EDITION QUANTITY: *3,030*
ITEM NUMBER: *Not Available*
HEIGHT: *5¼"*
MANUFACTURER: *Gerz, West Germany*
Decorated in USA
SPECIAL FEATURE: *Individually Numbered*

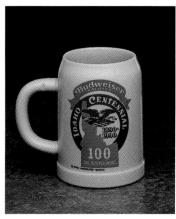

Daytona
Bud Speed Week

ISSUE YEAR: *1990*
EDITION QUANTITY: *4,005*
ITEM NUMBER: *Not Available*
HEIGHT: *5¼˝*
MANUFACTURER: *Gerz, West Germany Decorated in USA*
SPECIAL FEATURE: *Individually Numbered*

Idaho
Centennial

ISSUE YEAR: *1990*
EDITION QUANTITY: *2,736*
ITEM NUMBER: *SO49804*
HEIGHT: *5¼˝*
MANUFACTURER: *Gerz, West Germany Decorated in USA*
SPECIAL FEATURE: *Individually Numbered*

Seattle
Good Will Games

ISSUE YEAR: *1990*
EDITION QUANTITY: *1,824*
ITEM NUMBER: *SO47627*
HEIGHT: *5¼˝*
MANUFACTURER: *Gerz, West Germany Decorated in USA*
SPECIAL FEATURE: *Individually Numbered*

Michigan Ducks Unlimited Series
Duck
Lidded

ISSUE YEAR: *1990*
EDITION QUANTITY: *200*
ITEM NUMBER: *SO42208*
SERIES ORDER: *First*
HEIGHT: *6¾˝*
MANUFACTURER: *Made & Decorated in USA*
SPECIAL FEATURES: *Individually Numbered, Bottom Stamp, Gold Metallic Bands*

Introduction to Wisconsin
Wildlife Series
Duck

ISSUE YEAR: *1990*
EDITION QUANTITY: *200*
ITEM NUMBER: *Not Available*
HEIGHT: *5¼″*
MANUFACTURER: *Gerz, West Germany
Decorated in USA*
SPECIAL FEATURES: *Individually
Numbered, "Bud Barreling In
Wisconsin" noted on reverse side*

Wisconsin Wildlife Series
Deer

ISSUE YEAR: *1990*
EDITION QUANTITY: *3,708*
ITEM NUMBER: *SO49700*
SERIES ORDER: *First*
HEIGHT: *5¼″*
MANUFACTURER: *Gerz, West Germany
Decorated in USA*
SPECIAL FEATURE: *Individually
Numbered*

Wisconsin Wildlife Series
Duck

ISSUE YEAR: *1990*
EDITION QUANTITY: *3,264*
ITEM NUMBER: *SO49699*
SERIES ORDER: *First*
HEIGHT: *5¼″*
MANUFACTURER: *Gerz, West Germany
Decorated in USA*
SPECIAL FEATURE: *Individually
Numbered*

Wisconsin Wildlife Series
Turkey

ISSUE YEAR: *1990*
EDITION QUANTITY: *2,508*
ITEM NUMBER: *SO48249*
SERIES ORDER: *First*
HEIGHT: *5¼″*
MANUFACTURER: *Gerz, West Germany
Decorated in USA*
SPECIAL FEATURE: *Individually
Numbered*

Wisconsin Wildlife Series
Walleye

ISSUE YEAR: *1990*
EDITION QUANTITY: *3,214*
ITEM NUMBER: *SO49244*
SERIES ORDER: *First*
HEIGHT: *5¼″*
MANUFACTURER: *Gerz, West Germany*
Decorated in USA
SPECIAL FEATURE: *Individually Numbered*

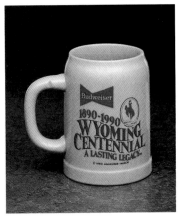

Wyoming
Centennial A & B

ISSUE YEAR: *1990*
EDITION QUANTITY: *A: 568, B: 748*
ITEM NUMBER: *A: SO49243,*
B: SO50138
HEIGHT: *5¼″*
MANUFACTURER: *Gerz, West Germany*
Decorated in USA
SPECIAL FEATURES: *A: Logo on Back of Stein, B: Scene on Back of Stein*

Arkansas
Rice/Duck

ISSUE YEAR: *1991*
EDITION QUANTITY: *2,172*
ITEM NUMBER: *SO51582*
HEIGHT: *5¼″*
MANUFACTURER: *Gerz, West Germany*
Decorated in USA
SPECIAL FEATURE: *Individually Numbered*

California
Big Bear Oktoberfest
21st Anniversary

ISSUE YEAR: *1991*
EDITION QUANTITY: *1,524*
ITEM NUMBER: *SO53954*
HEIGHT: *5¼″*
MANUFACTURER: *Gerz, West Germany*
Decorated in USA
SPECIAL FEATURE: *Individually Numbered*

1991

Colorado
And No Place Else

ISSUE YEAR: *1991*
EDITION QUANTITY: *2,754*
ITEM NUMBER: *SO52848*
HEIGHT: *5¼″*
MANUFACTURER: *Gerz, West Germany Decorated in USA*
SPECIAL FEATURE: *Individually Numbered*

Dodge City Days

ISSUE YEAR: *1991*
EDITION QUANTITY: *500*
ITEM NUMBER: *SO53465*
HEIGHT: *5¼″*
MANUFACTURER: *Gerz, West Germany Decorated in USA*

Oklahoma
Festival Of The Horse

ISSUE YEAR: *1991*
EDITION QUANTITY: *2,000*
ITEM NUMBER: *SO55447*
HEIGHT: *5¼″*
MANUFACTURER: *Gerz, West Germany Decorated in USA*
SPECIAL FEATURES: *Individually Numbered, Bottom Stamp*

San Antonio
Fiesta

ISSUE YEAR: *1991*
EDITION QUANTITY: *4,104*
ITEM NUMBER: *SO52190*
HEIGHT: *5¼″*
MANUFACTURER: *Gerz, West Germany Decorated in USA*
SPECIAL FEATURE: *Individually Numbered*

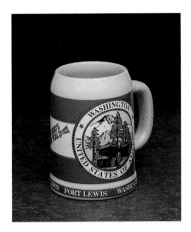

Fort Lewis Washington

ISSUE YEAR: *1991*
EDITION QUANTITY: *1,512*
ITEM NUMBER: *SO54147*
HEIGHT: *5¼"*
MANUFACTURER: *Gerz, West Germany
Decorated in USA*
SPECIAL FEATURE: *Individually Numbered*

Georgia Fishing
On My Mind

ISSUE YEAR: *1991*
EDITION QUANTITY: *1,476*
ITEM NUMBER: *SO53834*
HEIGHT: *5¼"*
MANUFACTURER: *Gerz, West Germany
Decorated in USA*
SPECIAL FEATURE: *Individually Numbered*

Georgia Hunting
On My Mind

ISSUE YEAR: *1991*
EDITION QUANTITY: *1,752*
ITEM NUMBER: *SO54141*
HEIGHT: *5¼"*
MANUFACTURER: *Gerz, West Germany
Decorated in USA*
SPECIAL FEATURE: *Individually Numbered*

Houston
Rodeo

ISSUE YEAR: *1991*
EDITION QUANTITY: *1,152*
ITEM NUMBER: *Not Available*
HEIGHT: *5¼"*
MANUFACTURER: *Gerz, West Germany
Decorated in USA*

1991

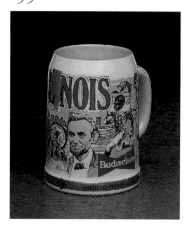

Illinois State

ISSUE YEAR: *1991*
EDITION QUANTITY: *4,968*
ITEM NUMBER: *SO54808*
HEIGHT: *5¼″*
MANUFACTURER: *Gerz, West Germany Decorated in USA*
SPECIAL FEATURE: *Individually Numbered*

Kansas
Good To Know You

ISSUE YEAR: *1991*
EDITION QUANTITY: *3,708*
ITEM NUMBER: *SO53618*
HEIGHT: *5¼″*
MANUFACTURER: *Gerz, West Germany Decorated in USA*
SPECIAL FEATURE: *Individually Numbered*

Kentucky
The Celebration

ISSUE YEAR: *1991*
EDITION QUANTITY: *3,732*
ITEM NUMBER: *SO54022*
HEIGHT: *5¼″*
MANUFACTURER: *Gerz, West Germany Decorated in USA*
SPECIAL FEATURE: *Individually Numbered*

Mardi Gras
Nothing Beats A Bud

ISSUE YEAR: *1991*
EDITION QUANTITY: *6,000*
ITEM NUMBER: *SO50500*
HEIGHT: *5¼″*
MANUFACTURER: *Gerz, West Germany Decorated in USA*
SPECIAL FEATURE: *Individually Numbered*

Photo not
available

Michigan Ducks Unlimited Series
Loon
Lidded

ISSUE YEAR: *1991*
EDITION QUANTITY: *220*
ITEM NUMBER: *SO54807*
SERIES ORDER: *Second*
HEIGHT: *6¾″*
MANUFACTURER: *Made & Decorated
in USA*
SPECIAL FEATURES: *Individually
Numbered, Bottom Stamp, Gold Bands*
ARTIST: *Rick Kelly*

Minnesota Wildlife Series
Loon

ISSUE YEAR: *1991*
EDITION QUANTITY: *4,776*
ITEM NUMBER: *SO53143*
SERIES ORDER: *First*
HEIGHT: *5¾″*
MANUFACTURER: *Made & Decorated
in USA*
SPECIAL FEATURES: *Individually
Numbered, Bottom Stamp, Gold Bands*
ARTIST: *Jerry Raedeke*

Mississippi Bass
Always In Season

ISSUE YEAR: *1991*
EDITION QUANTITY: *1,152*
ITEM NUMBER: *SO54822*
HEIGHT: *5¼″*
MANUFACTURER: *Gerz, West Germany
Decorated in USA*
SPECIAL FEATURE: *Individually
Numbered*

Mississippi Deer
Always In Season

ISSUE YEAR: *1991*
EDITION QUANTITY: *1,308*
ITEM NUMBER: *SO54806*
HEIGHT: *5¼″*
MANUFACTURER: *Gerz, West Germany
Decorated in USA*
SPECIAL FEATURES: *Individually
Numbered, Bottom Stamp*

1991

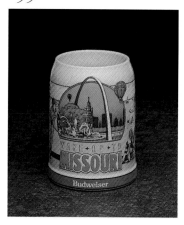

Missouri
Wake Up To Missouri

ISSUE YEAR: *1991*
EDITION QUANTITY: *3,228*
ITEM NUMBER: *SO54149*
HEIGHT: *5¼″*
MANUFACTURER: *Gerz, West Germany Decorated in USA*
SPECIAL FEATURE: *Individually Numbered*

Nebraska
Traditions

ISSUE YEAR: *1991*
EDITION QUANTITY: *8,208*
ITEM NUMBER: *SO50512*
HEIGHT: *5¼″*
MANUFACTURER: *Gerz, West Germany Decorated in USA*
SPECIAL FEATURE: *Individually Numbered*

New York
A State Of Mind

ISSUE YEAR: *1991*
EDITION QUANTITY: *1,749*
ITEM NUMBER: *SO54214*
HEIGHT: *5¼″*
MANUFACTURER: *Gerz, West Germany Decorated in USA*
SPECIAL FEATURE: *Individually Numbered*

Ohio
The Heart Of It All

ISSUE YEAR: *1991*
EDITION QUANTITY: *4,068*
ITEM NUMBER: *SO55446*
HEIGHT: *5¼″*
MANUFACTURER: *Gerz, West Germany Decorated in USA*
SPECIAL FEATURES: *Individually Numbered, Bottom Stamp*

Oklahoma
Better Sooner Than Later

ISSUE YEAR: *1991*
EDITION QUANTITY: *2,676*
ITEM NUMBER: *SO53689*
HEIGHT: *5¼″*
MANUFACTURER: *Gerz, West Germany Decorated in USA*
SPECIAL FEATURE: *Individually Numbered*

Oktoberfest

ISSUE YEAR: *1991*
EDITION QUANTITY: *Open*
ITEM NUMBER: *SO54077*
SERIES ORDER: *First*
HEIGHT: *5¼″*
MANUFACTURER: *Gerz, West Germany Decorated in USA*
SPECIAL FEATURES: *Individually Numbered, Bottom Stamp*

Pennsylvania
A State For All Seasons

ISSUE YEAR: *1991*
EDITION QUANTITY: *3,288*
ITEM NUMBER: *SO54215*
HEIGHT: *5¼″*
MANUFACTURER: *Gerz, West Germany Decorated in USA*
SPECIAL FEATURE: *Individually Numbered*

Redlands
Chili Cook-Off

ISSUE YEAR: *1991*
EDITION QUANTITY: *1,404*
ITEM NUMBER: *SO53757*
HEIGHT: *5¼″*
MANUFACTURER: *Gerz, West Germany Decorated in USA*
SPECIAL FEATURE: *Individually Numbered*

1991

Save The Bay I

Save The Lake Pontchartrain

ISSUE YEAR: *1991*
EDITION QUANTITY: *10,261*
ITEM NUMBER: *SO52286*
HEIGHT: *7¼″*
MANUFACTURER: *Made & Decorated in USA*
SPECIAL FEATURE: *Individually Numbered, Bottom Stamp, Gold Metallic Bands*
ARTIST: *Martha Hudson*

ISSUE YEAR: *1991*
EDITION QUANTITY: *5,000*
ITEM NUMBER: *SO54240*
SERIES ORDER: *First*
HEIGHT: *5¾″*
MANUFACTURER: *Made & Decorated in USA*
SPECIAL FEATURES: *Individually Numbered, Bottom Stamp, Gold Bands*
ARTIST: *Peter Briant*

Temecula
Tractor Race

Utah
Naturally

ISSUE YEAR: *1991*
EDITION QUANTITY: *1,404*
ITEM NUMBER: *SO53847*
HEIGHT: *5¼″*
MANUFACTURER: *Gerz, West Germany Decorated in USA*
SPECIAL FEATURE: *Individually Numbered*

ISSUE YEAR: *1991*
EDITION QUANTITY: *2,246*
ITEM NUMBER: *SO52847*
HEIGHT: *5¼″*
MANUFACTURER: *Gerz, West Germany Decorated in USA*
SPECIAL FEATURE: *Individually Numbered*

Vermont
Bicentennial

ISSUE YEAR: *1991*
EDITION QUANTITY: *3,192*
ITEM NUMBER: *SO53758*
HEIGHT: *5¼″*
MANUFACTURER: *Gerz, West Germany
Decorated in USA*
SPECIAL FEATURE: *Individually
Numbered*

Wisconsin Wildlife Series
Best Beer~Best Deer
Lidded

ISSUE YEAR: *1991*
EDITION QUANTITY: *1,872*
ITEM NUMBER: *SO55713*
SERIES ORDER: *Second*
HEIGHT: *6¾″*
MANUFACTURER: *Made & Decorated
in USA*
SPECIAL FEATURES: *Individually
Numbered, Bottom Stamp, Pewter
Metallic Bands*

Alabama State

Athens, New York
Firefighters

ISSUE YEAR: *1992*
EDITION QUANTITY: *2,000*
ITEM NUMBER: *SO64282*
HEIGHT: *5¼″*
MANUFACTURER: *Gerz, West Germany
Decorated in USA*
SPECIAL FEATURES: *Individually
Numbered, Bottom Stamp*

ISSUE YEAR: *1992*
EDITION QUANTITY: *2,100*
ITEM NUMBER: *SO64209*
HEIGHT: *5¼″*
MANUFACTURER: *Gerz, West Germany
Decorated in USA*
SPECIAL FEATURE: *Bottom Stamp*

1992

Budweiser Burns Coal

Budweiser Racing

ISSUE YEAR: *1992*
EDITION QUANTITY: *4,500*
ITEM NUMBER: *SO64374*
HEIGHT: *5¼″*
MANUFACTURER: *Gerz, West Germany Decorated in USA*
SPECIAL FEATURES: *Individually Numbered, Bottom Stamp*

ISSUE YEAR: *1992*
EDITION QUANTITY: *Open*
ITEM NUMBER: *N3553 & SO63790*
SERIES ORDER: *First*
HEIGHT: *5¾″*
MANUFACTURER: *Made & Decorated in USA*
SPECIAL FEATURES: *Individually Numbered, Bottom Stamp*

Cardinals
100th Anniversary

Cincinnati
Tallstacks

ISSUE YEAR: *1992*
EDITION QUANTITY: *10,000*
ITEM NUMBER: *N3767*
HEIGHT: *5¼″*
MANUFACTURER: *Gerz, West Germany Decorated in USA*
SPECIAL FEATURES: *Individually Numbered, Bottom Stamp*

ISSUE YEAR: *1992*
EDITION QUANTITY: *1,100*
ITEM NUMBER: *N3942*
HEIGHT: *5¼″*
MANUFACTURER: *Gerz, West Germany Decorated in USA*
SPECIAL FEATURES: *Individually Numbered, Bottom Stamp*

Du Quoin
State Fair

ISSUE YEAR: *1992*
EDITION QUANTITY: *1,000*
ITEM NUMBER: *N3941*
HEIGHT: *5¾″*
MANUFACTURER: *Made & Decorated in USA*
SPECIAL FEATURES: *Individually Numbered, Bottom Stamp, Gold Metallic Bands*

Georgia
Bass

ISSUE YEAR: *1992*
EDITION QUANTITY: *744*
ITEM NUMBER: *SO63840*
HEIGHT: *5¼″*
MANUFACTURER: *Gerz, West Germany Decorated in USA*
SPECIAL FEATURES: *Individually Numbered, Bottom Stamp*

Photo not available

Georgia
Deer

ISSUE YEAR: *1992*
EDITION QUANTITY: *732*
ITEM NUMBER: *SO64054*
HEIGHT: *5¼″*
MANUFACTURER: *Gerz, West Germany Decorated in USA*
SPECIAL FEATURES: *Individually Numbered, Bottom Stamp*

Indiana
Crossroads Of America

ISSUE YEAR: *1992*
EDITION QUANTITY: *1,100*
ITEM NUMBER: *SO68206*
HEIGHT: *5¼″*
MANUFACTURER: *Gerz, West Germany Decorated in USA*
SPECIAL FEATURES: *Individually Numbered, Bottom Stamp*

1992

Iowa
The Time Is Right

ISSUE YEAR: *1992*
EDITION QUANTITY: *3,480*
ITEM NUMBER: *SO67816*
HEIGHT: *5¼"*
MANUFACTURER: *Gerz, West Germany*
Decorated in USA
SPECIAL FEATURES: *Individually Numbered, Bottom Stamp*

It's A Bud Thing

ISSUE YEAR: *1992*
EDITION QUANTITY: *500*
ITEM NUMBER: *N3645*
HEIGHT: *5¼"*
MANUFACTURER: *Gerz, West Germany*
Decorated in USA
SPECIAL FEATURE: *Individually Numbered*

Louisiana
We're Really Cookin'

ISSUE YEAR: *1992*
EDITION QUANTITY: *3,600*
ITEM NUMBER: *SO67814*
HEIGHT: *5¼"*
MANUFACTURER: *Gerz, West Germany*
Decorated in USA
SPECIAL FEATURES: *Individually Numbered, Bottom Stamp*

Mardi Gras
Bud Mardi Gras '92

ISSUE YEAR: *1992*
EDITION QUANTITY: *10,000*
ITEM NUMBER: *SO56219*
HEIGHT: *5¼"*
MANUFACTURER: *Gerz, West Germany*
Decorated in USA
SPECIAL FEATURES: *Individually Numbered, Bottom Stamp*

*Michigan Ducks Unlimited
Wholesaler Series*

Duck
Lidded

ISSUE YEAR: *1992*
EDITION QUANTITY: *3,000*
ITEM NUMBER: *SO64169*
SERIES ORDER: *First*
HEIGHT: *6¾"*
MANUFACTURER: *Made & Decorated in USA*
SPECIAL FEATURES: *Individually Numbered, Bottom Stamp, Pewter Bands*
ARTIST: *Rick Kelly*

Michigan Ducks Unlimited Series

Swan
Lidded

ISSUE YEAR: *1992*
EDITION QUANTITY: *220*
ITEM NUMBER: *N3828*
SERIES ORDER: *Third*
HEIGHT: *6¾"*
MANUFACTURER: *Made & Decorated in USA*
SPECIAL FEATURES: *Individually Numbered, Bottom Stamp, Gold Bands*
ARTIST: *Rick Kelly*

Minnesota Wildlife Series

Mallard

ISSUE YEAR: *1992*
EDITION QUANTITY: *6,000*
ITEM NUMBER: *SO67817*
SERIES ORDER: *Second*
HEIGHT: *5¾"*
MANUFACTURER: *Made & Decorated in USA*
SPECIAL FEATURES: *Individually Numbered, Bottom Stamp, Gold Bands*
ARTIST: *Jerry Raedeke*

New York State II

ISSUE YEAR: *1992*
EDITION QUANTITY: *1,368*
ITEM NUMBER: *SO67694*
HEIGHT: *5¼"*
MANUFACTURER: *Gerz, West Germany Decorated in USA*
SPECIAL FEATURES: *Individually Numbered, Bottom Stamp*

1992

North Carolina
Carolina On My Mind

ISSUE YEAR: *1992*
EDITION QUANTITY: *984*
ITEM NUMBER: *SO64215*
HEIGHT: *5¾″*
MANUFACTURER: *Made & Decorated in USA*
SPECIAL FEATURE: *Individually Numbered*

O'Doul's
What Beer Drinkers Drink

ISSUE YEAR: *1992*
EDITION QUANTITY: *10,000*
ITEM NUMBER: *N3522 & N3522D*
HEIGHT: *5¼″*
MANUFACTURER: *Gerz, West Germany Decorated in USA*
SPECIAL FEATURES: *Individually Numbered, Bottom Stamp*

Puerto Rico
Quinto Centenario

ISSUE YEAR: *1992*
EDITION QUANTITY: *11,000*
ITEM NUMBER: *SO65691*
HEIGHT: *5½″*
MANUFACTURER: *Ceramarte, Brazil*
SPECIAL FEATURE: *Full Relief*

Tennessee
We're Playing Your Song

ISSUE YEAR: *1992*
EDITION QUANTITY: *1,150*
ITEM NUMBER: *SO63887*
HEIGHT: *5¼″*
MANUFACTURER: *Made & Decorated in USA*
SPECIAL FEATURE: *Individually Numbered*

Texas
Living Free In Texas

ISSUE YEAR: *1992*
EDITION QUANTITY: *Open*
ITEM NUMBER: *SO64487 & N3648*
HEIGHT: *7¼"*
MANUFACTURER: *Made & Decorated in USA*
SPECIAL FEATURES: *Individually Numbered, Bottom Stamp, Gold Decal on Thumbrest*

West Texas
Centennial

ISSUE YEAR: *1992*
EDITION QUANTITY: *1,500*
ITEM NUMBER: *N3943*
HEIGHT: *5¼"*
MANUFACTURER: *Gerz, West Germany Decorated in USA*
SPECIAL FEATURES: *Individually Numbered, Bottom Stamp*

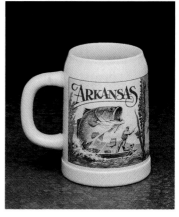

Albuquerque Balloon Fiesta
Magic in the Air

ISSUE YEAR: *1993*
EDITION QUANTITY: *3,668*
ITEM NUMBER: *N4247*
HEIGHT: *7"*
MANUFACTURER: *Made & Decorated in USA*
SPECIAL FEATURES: *Individually Numbered, Bottom Stamp*
ARTIST: *Bud Kemper*

Arkansas
Brewed With Rice

ISSUE YEAR: *1993*
EDITION QUANTITY: *3,000*
ITEM NUMBER: *N3940*
HEIGHT: *5½"*
MANUFACTURER: *Gerz, West Germany Decorated in USA*
SPECIAL FEATURES: *Individually Numbered, Bottom Stamp*

1993

Chiefs of Police
100th Anniversary

ISSUE YEAR: *1993*
EDITION QUANTITY: *9,000*
ITEM NUMBER: *N3589*
HEIGHT: *5¼″*
MANUFACTURER: *Gerz, West Germany Decorated in USA*
SPECIAL FEATURES: *Individually Numbered, Bottom Stamp*

Colorado Ducks Unlimited Series
Mallard
Lidded

ISSUE YEAR: *1993*
EDITION QUANTITY: *100*
ITEM NUMBER: *N4252*
HEIGHT: *6¾″*
MANUFACTURER: *Gerz, West Germany Decorated in USA*
SPECIAL FEATURES: *Individually Numbered, Bottom Stamp*

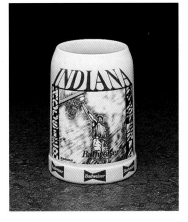

Illinois
Sportsmen

ISSUE YEAR: *1993*
EDITION QUANTITY: *826*
ITEM NUMBER: *N4241*
HEIGHT: *5½″*
MANUFACTURER: *Made & Decorated in USA*
SPECIAL FEATURES: *Individually Numbered, Bottom Stamp*

Indiana
Hoosier Hysteria

ISSUE YEAR: *1993*
EDITION QUANTITY: *1359*
ITEM NUMBER: *N4242*
HEIGHT: *5¼″*
MANUFACTURER: *Gerz, West Germany Decorated in USA*
SPECIAL FEATURES: *Individually Numbered, Bottom Stamp*

Mardi Gras
1993

ISSUE YEAR: *1993*
EDITION QUANTITY: *3,200*
ITEM NUMBER: *N4073*
HEIGHT: *5¼″*
MANUFACTURER: *Gerz, West Germany
Decorated in USA*
SPECIAL FEATURES: *Individually
Numbered, Bottom Stamp*

Michigan Ducks Unlimited Series
Heron
Lidded

ISSUE YEAR: *1993*
EDITION QUANTITY: *220*
ITEM NUMBER: *N4251*
SERIES ORDER: *Fourth*
HEIGHT: *6¾″*
MANUFACTURER: *Made & Decorated
in USA*
SPECIAL FEATURES: *Individually
Numbered, Bottom Stamp*
ARTIST: *Rick Kelly*

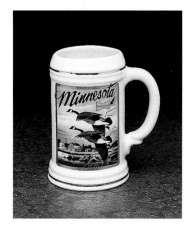

Minnesota Wildlife Series
Canada Geese

ISSUE YEAR: *1993*
EDITION QUANTITY: *3,296*
ITEM NUMBER: *N4250*
SERIES ORDER: *Third*
HEIGHT: *5½″*
MANUFACTURER: *Made & Decorated
in USA*
SPECIAL FEATURES: *Individually
Numbered, Bottom Stamp, Gold Bands*
ARTIST: *Jerry Raedeke*

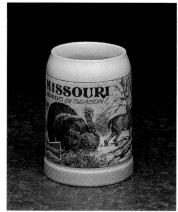

Missouri
Always In Season

ISSUE YEAR: *1993*
EDITION QUANTITY: *3,000*
ITEM NUMBER: *N4118*
HEIGHT: *5¼″*
MANUFACTURER: *Gerz, West Germany
Decorated in USA*
SPECIAL FEATURES: *Individually
Numbered, Bottom Stamp*

1993

Nebraska
Wildlife

ISSUE YEAR: *1993*
EDITION QUANTITY: *3,000*
ITEM NUMBER: *N4117*
HEIGHT: *5¼″*
MANUFACTURER: *Gerz, West Germany Decorated in USA*
SPECIAL FEATURES: *Individually Numbered, Bottom Stamp*

Ohio Jaycees
Partners In Leadership Development

ISSUE YEAR: *1993*
EDITION QUANTITY: *1,000*
ITEM NUMBER: *N4119*
HEIGHT: *5¾″*
MANUFACTURER: *Made & Decorated in USA*
SPECIAL FEATURES: *Individually Numbered, Bottom Stamp*

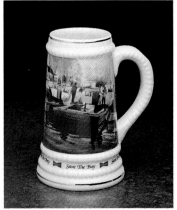

Phoenix
One Million Barrels

ISSUE YEAR: *1993*
EDITION QUANTITY: *650*
ITEM NUMBER: *N4105*
HEIGHT: *7¼″*
MANUFACTURER: *Made & Decorated in USA*
SPECIAL FEATURES: *Individually Numbered, Bottom Stamp*

Save The Bay II

ISSUE YEAR: *1993*
EDITION QUANTITY: *5,860*
ITEM NUMBER: *N4120*
HEIGHT: *7¼″*
MANUFACTURER: *Made & Decorated in USA*
SPECIAL FEATURES: *Individually Numbered, Bottom Stamp, Gold Bands, Gold A&Eagle Decal on Thumbrest*
ARTIST: *Lee A. Boynton*

United Way 1993 Fair Share

ISSUE YEAR: *1993*
EDITION QUANTITY: *1,000*
ITEM NUMBER: *N4121*
HEIGHT: *7″*
MANUFACTURER: *Made & Decorated in USA*
SPECIAL FEATURES: *Individually Numbered, Bottom Stamp*

Wisconsin
Vince Lombardi
Lidded

ISSUE YEAR: *1993*
EDITION QUANTITY: *4,287*
ITEM NUMBER: *N4249*
HEIGHT: *6¾″*
MANUFACTURER: *Made & Decorated in USA*
SPECIAL FEATURES: *Individually Numbered, Gold Lid, Bottom Stamp*
ARTIST: *Susan Sampson*

Wisconsin
Waterfowl - Gold Lid

ISSUE YEAR: *1993*
EDITION QUANTITY: *1728*
ITEM NUMBER: *N4248G*
HEIGHT: *6¾″*
MANUFACTURER: *Made & Decorated in USA*
SPECIAL FEATURES: *Gold Lid, Individually Numbered, Bottom Stamp*

Wisconsin
Waterfowl - Pewter Lid

ISSUE YEAR: *1993*
EDITION QUANTITY: *1,528*
ITEM NUMBER: *N4248P*
HEIGHT: *6¾″*
MANUFACTURER: *Made & Decorated in USA*
SPECIAL FEATURES: *Pewter Lid, Individually Numbered, Bottom Stamp*

1994

Budweiser Brickyard 400
Inaugural Race

ISSUE YEAR: *1994*
EDITION QUANTITY: *7,500*
ITEM NUMBER: *N4822*
SERIES ORDER: *First*
HEIGHT: *5¼″*
MANUFACTURER: *Gerz, West Germany Decorated in USA*
SPECIAL FEATURES: *Individually Numbered, Bottom Stamp*

Colorado Ducks Unlimited Series
Wood Duck
Lidded

ISSUE YEAR: *1994*
EDITION QUANTITY: *124*
ITEM NUMBER: *N4998*
SERIES ORDER: *Second*
HEIGHT: *6¾″*
MANUFACTURER: *Made & Decorated in USA*
SPECIAL FEATURES: *Individually Numbered, Bottom Stamp*

Mardi Gras
1994

ISSUE YEAR: *1994*
EDITION QUANTITY: *3,000*
ITEM NUMBER: *N4467*
HEIGHT: *5¼″*
MANUFACTURER: *Gerz, West Germany Decorated in USA*
SPECIAL FEATURES: *Individually Numbered, Bottom Stamp*

Michigan Ducks Unlimited Series
Gadwall Duck

ISSUE YEAR: *1994*
EDITION QUANTITY: *220*
ITEM NUMBER: *N4903S*
SERIES ORDER: *Fifth*
HEIGHT: *5½″*
MANUFACTURER: *Made & Decorated in USA*
SPECIAL FEATURES: *Individually Numbered, Bottom Stamp*
ARTIST: *Rick Kelly*

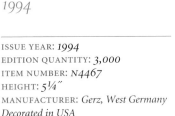

National Hobo Convention

ISSUE YEAR: *1994*
EDITION QUANTITY: *750*
ITEM NUMBER: *SO84670*
HEIGHT: *5½″*
MANUFACTURER: *Made & Decorated in USA*
SPECIAL FEATURES: *Individually Numbered, Bottom Stamp*

United States JCI Senate

ISSUE YEAR: *1994*
EDITION QUANTITY: *1,364*
ITEM NUMBER: *SO82138*
HEIGHT: *5½″*
MANUFACTURER: *Made & Decorated in USA*
SPECIAL FEATURES: *Individually Numbered, Bottom Stamp*

United Way 1994 Fair Share

Lidded

ISSUE YEAR: *1994*
EDITION QUANTITY: *1,300*
ITEM NUMBER: *SO84542*
HEIGHT: *8¼″*
MANUFACTURER: *Made & Decorated in USA*
SPECIAL FEATURES: *Pewter Lid with Eagle Figurine On Top, Individually Numbered, Bottom Stamp*

World Cup USA '94

Boston

ISSUE YEAR: *1994*
EDITION QUANTITY: *620*
ITEM NUMBER: *N4559*
HEIGHT: *6¾″*
MANUFACTURER: *Ceramarte, Brazil*
SPECIAL FEATURES: *Individually Numbered, Bottom Stamp*

1994

World Cup USA '94
Chicago

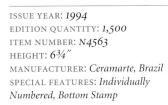

ISSUE YEAR: *1994*
EDITION QUANTITY: *1,500*
ITEM NUMBER: *N4563*
HEIGHT: *6¾"*
MANUFACTURER: *Ceramarte, Brazil*
SPECIAL FEATURES: *Individually Numbered, Bottom Stamp*

World Cup USA '94
Dallas

ISSUE YEAR: *1994*
EDITION QUANTITY: *620*
ITEM NUMBER: *N4565*
HEIGHT: *6¾"*
MANUFACTURER: *Ceramarte, Brazil*
SPECIAL FEATURES: *Individually Numbered, Bottom Stamp*

World Cup USA '94
Detroit

ISSUE YEAR: *1994*
EDITION QUANTITY: *1,500*
ITEM NUMBER: *N4561*
HEIGHT: *6¾"*
MANUFACTURER: *Ceramarte, Brazil*
SPECIAL FEATURES: *Individually Numbered, Bottom Stamp*

World Cup USA '94
Los Angeles

ISSUE YEAR: *1994*
EDITION QUANTITY: *2,516*
ITEM NUMBER: *N4558*
HEIGHT: *6¾"*
MANUFACTURER: *Ceramarte, Brazil*
SPECIAL FEATURES: *Individually Numbered, Bottom Stamp*

World Cup USA '94
New York/New Jersey

ISSUE YEAR: *1994*
EDITION QUANTITY: *620*
ITEM NUMBER: *N4560*
HEIGHT: *6¾"*
MANUFACTURER: *Ceramarte, Brazil*
SPECIAL FEATURES: *Individually Numbered, Bottom Stamp*

World Cup USA '94
Orlando

ISSUE YEAR: *1994*
EDITION QUANTITY: *5,304*
ITEM NUMBER: *N4564*
HEIGHT: *6¾"*
MANUFACTURER: *Ceramarte, Brazil*
SPECIAL FEATURES: *Individually Numbered, Bottom Stamp*

World Cup USA '94
San Francisco

ISSUE YEAR: *1994*
EDITION QUANTITY: *1,044*
ITEM NUMBER: *N4562*
HEIGHT: *6¾"*
MANUFACTURER: *Ceramarte, Brazil*
SPECIAL FEATURES: *Individually Numbered, Bottom Stamp*

World Cup USA '94
Washington, DC

ISSUE YEAR: *1994*
EDITION QUANTITY: *620*
ITEM NUMBER: *N4566*
HEIGHT: *6¾"*
MANUFACTURER: *Ceramarte, Brazil*
SPECIAL FEATURES: *Individually Numbered, Bottom Stamp*

1995

Anheuser-Busch Golf Classic
Colorado Easter Seal Society

ISSUE YEAR: *1995*
EDITION QUANTITY: *150*
ITEM NUMBER: *SO862779*
HEIGHT: *5¼″*
MANUFACTURER: *Gerz, West Germany Decorated in USA*
SPECIAL FEATURES: *Individually Numbered, Bottom Stamp*
ARTIST: *Ellie Weakley*

Anheuser-Busch Recycling
5 Billion Pounds

ISSUE YEAR: *1995*
EDITION QUANTITY: *960*
ITEM NUMBER: *SO86266*
HEIGHT: *5¼″*
MANUFACTURER: *Gerz, West Germany Decorated in USA*
SPECIAL FEATURES: *Individually Numbered, Bottom Stamp*

Budweiser Brickyard 400

ISSUE YEAR: *1995*
EDITION QUANTITY: *5,000*
ITEM NUMBER: *N5359*
SERIES ORDER: *Second*
HEIGHT: *5¼″*
MANUFACTURER: *Gerz, West Germany Decorated in USA*
SPECIAL FEATURES: *Individually Numbered, Bottom Stamp*

Budweiser Chip Hanauer

ISSUE YEAR: *1995*
EDITION QUANTITY: *Open*
ITEM NUMBER: *N5511*
HEIGHT: *5¼″*
MANUFACTURER: *Gerz, West Germany Decorated in USA*
SPECIAL FEATURES: *Open Edition, Bottom Stamp, Gold Trim and Detailing*

Bud-weis-er Frogs

Budweiser Kenny Bernstein

ISSUE YEAR: *1995*
EDITION QUANTITY: *10,000*
ITEM NUMBER: *N5402*
HEIGHT: *5¼″*
MANUFACTURER: *Gerz, West Germany Decorated in USA*
SPECIAL FEATURES: *Individually Numbered, Bottom Stamp*

ISSUE YEAR: *1995*
EDITION QUANTITY: *Open*
ITEM NUMBER: *N5512*
HEIGHT: *5¼″*
MANUFACTURER: *Gerz, West Germany Decorated in USA*
SPECIAL FEATURES: *Open Edition, Bottom Stamp, Gold Trim and Detailing*

Budweiser Ken Schrader

Budweiser Ken Schrader

ISSUE YEAR: *1995*
EDITION QUANTITY: *4,400*
ITEM NUMBER: *N5054*
HEIGHT: *5¼″*
MANUFACTURER: *Gerz, West Germany Decorated in USA*
SPECIAL FEATURE: *Bottom Stamp*

ISSUE YEAR: *1995*
EDITION QUANTITY: *Open*
ITEM NUMBER: *N5510*
HEIGHT: *5¼″*
MANUFACTURER: *Gerz, West Germany Decorated in USA*
SPECIAL FEATURES: *Open Edition, Bottom Stamp, Gold Trim and Detailing*

1995

Budweiser
Rodeo

ISSUE YEAR: *1995*
EDITION QUANTITY: *770*
ITEM NUMBER: *N5205*
HEIGHT: 5¼″
MANUFACTURER: *Gerz, West Germany
Decorated in USA*
SPECIAL FEATURES: *Individually
Numbered, Bottom Stamp*

California
Big Bear Oktoberfest
25th Anniversary

ISSUE YEAR: *1995*
EDITION QUANTITY: *700*
ITEM NUMBER: *SO86916*
HEIGHT: 5¼″
MANUFACTURER: *Gerz, West Germany
Decorated in USA*
SPECIAL FEATURE: *Hand Numbered*

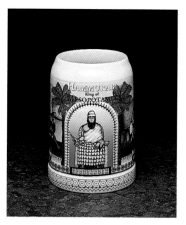

Chaldean & Ohio
Hammurabi King
of Mesopotamia

ISSUE YEAR: *1995*
EDITION QUANTITY: *500*
ITEM NUMBER: *SO862781*
HEIGHT: 5¼″
MANUFACTURER: *Gerz, West Germany
Decorated in USA*
SPECIAL FEATURES: *Individually
Numbered, Bottom Stamp*

Colorado

ISSUE YEAR: *1995*
EDITION QUANTITY: *1,000*
ITEM NUMBER: *SO86539*
HEIGHT: 5¼″
MANUFACTURER: *Made & Decorated
in USA*
SPECIAL FEATURES: *Individually
Numbered, Bottom Stamp*

Colorado Ducks Unlimited Series
Goose
Lidded

ISSUE YEAR: *1995*
EDITION QUANTITY: *124*
ITEM NUMBER: *SO86531*
SERIES ORDER: *Third*
HEIGHT: *6¾″*
MANUFACTURER: *Made & Decorated in USA*
SPECIAL FEATURES: *Individually Numbered, Bottom Stamp*

Faust Beer

ISSUE YEAR: *1995*
EDITION QUANTITY: *2,200*
ITEM NUMBER: *SO94855*
HEIGHT: *5¼″*
MANUFACTURER: *Gerz, West Germany Decorated in USA*
SPECIAL FEATURES: *Individually Numbered, Bottom Stamp*

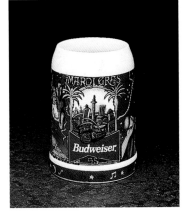

Houston
Texas Pride

ISSUE YEAR: *1995*
EDITION QUANTITY: *1,024*
ITEM NUMBER: *SO86865*
HEIGHT: *5½″*
MANUFACTURER: *Made & Decorated in USA*
SPECIAL FEATURES: *Individually Numbered, Bottom Stamp*

Mardi Gras
1995

ISSUE YEAR: *1995*
EDITION QUANTITY: *1,000*
ITEM NUMBER: *SO86277*
HEIGHT: *5¼″*
MANUFACTURER: *Gerz, West Germany Decorated in USA*
SPECIAL FEATURES: *Individually Numbered, Bottom Stamp*

1995

Michigan
12th World Hot Air Balloon Championship

ISSUE YEAR: *1995*
EDITION QUANTITY: *3,000*
ITEM NUMBER: *SO86475*
HEIGHT: *5¼″*
MANUFACTURER: *Gerz, West Germany Decorated in USA*
SPECIAL FEATURES: *Individually Numbered, Bottom Stamp*
ARTIST: *Don "Keg" KegLovitz*

Minnesota Wildlife Series
Pheasants

ISSUE YEAR: *1995*
EDITION QUANTITY: *2,624*
ITEM NUMBER: *SO86279*
SERIES ORDER: *Fourth*
HEIGHT: *5½″*
MANUFACTURER: *Made & Decorated in USA*
SPECIAL FEATURES: *Individually Numbered, Bottom Stamp, Gold Bands*
ARTIST: *Jerry Raedeke*

Nebraska Ducks Unlimited Series
Goose
Lidded

ISSUE YEAR: *1995*
EDITION QUANTITY: *125*
ITEM NUMBER: *SO86532*
SERIES ORDER: *First*
HEIGHT: *6¾″*
MANUFACTURER: *Made & Decorated in USA*
SPECIAL FEATURES: *Individually Numbered, Bottom Stamp*

Ohio Sportsmen

ISSUE YEAR: *1995*
EDITION QUANTITY: *600*
ITEM NUMBER: *SO862780*
HEIGHT: *5¼″*
MANUFACTURER: *Gerz, West Germany Decorated in USA*
SPECIAL FEATURES: *Individually Numbered, Bottom Stamp*

Rumble on the River
12th Annual

ISSUE YEAR: *1995*
EDITION QUANTITY: *3,000*
ITEM NUMBER: *SO86506*
HEIGHT: *5¼"*
MANUFACTURER: *Gerz, West Germany*
Decorated in USA
SPECIAL FEATURES: *Individually*
Numbered, Bottom Stamp
ARTIST: *Jim Wayneright*

Spencer Gifts' Christmas Meeting
Sea World

ISSUE YEAR: *1995*
EDITION QUANTITY: *700*
ITEM NUMBER: *N3264*
HEIGHT: *5¼"*
MANUFACTURER: *Gerz, West Germany*
Decorated in USA
SPECIAL FEATURES: *Individually*
Numbered, Bottom Stamp

Tennessee

ISSUE YEAR: *1995*
EDITION QUANTITY: *540*
ITEM NUMBER: *SO85008*
HEIGHT: *5½"*
MANUFACTURER: *Made & Decorated*
in USA
SPECIAL FEATURES: *Individually*
Numbered, Bottom Stamp

Item Number/Year Index

NOTE: *Several of the Item Numbers were assigned to steins which were in development, yet never produced, and some of the Item Numbers have been assigned to several steins which are currently in production.*

YEAR:	ITEM #:	NAME:	STATUS:	PAGE:
1990	BG1	Busch Gardens Extinction is Forever II	A*	200
1992	BG2	Busch Gardens Extinction is Forever III	A	201
1995	CB1	Budweiser Clydesdales at the Bauernhof Lidded	N/A	235
1995	CB2	The Brew House Clock Tower Lidded	A	236
1996	CB3	World's Largest Brewer Lidded	A	237
1996	CB4	King – A Regal Spirit Lidded	A	238
1975	CS1	Bud Man – 1975 Style Lidded	N/A	114
1976	CS2	A&Eagle	N/A	35
1976	CSL2	A&Eagle Lidded (reference CS28)	N/A	36
1976	CS3	Katakombe	N/A	15
1976	CSL3	Katakombe Lidded	N/A	16
1976	CS4	German Tavern Scene	N/A	17
1975	CSL4	Senior Grande Lidded	N/A	18
1975	CS5	German Pilique	N/A	19
1976	CSL5	German Pilique Lidded	N/A	20
1977	CS6	Senior Grande	N/A	21
1975	CSL6	German Tavern Scene Lidded	N/A	22
	CS7	No Documentation Available		
1976	CSL7	Budweiser Centennial Lidded	N/A	23
N/A	CS8	Mini Mug Set Of Four	N/A	263
1976	CSL8	U.S. Bicentennial Lidded	N/A	24
1977	CS9	Natural Light	N/A	117
1976	CSL9	Clydesdales Lidded	N/A	61
	CS10	No Documentation Available		
	CS11	No Documentation Available		
1976	CS12	Clydesdales	N/A	263
1976	CS13	Budweiser Centennial	N/A	25
1976	CS14	U.S. Bicentennial	N/A	26
1976	CS15	Clydesdales	N/A	62
	CS16	No Documentation Available		
	CS17	No Documentation Available		
1976	CS18	Budweiser Label	N/A	118
1980	CS19	Budweiser Champion Clydesdales	N/A	41
1981	CS19A	Budweiser Champion Clydesdales	N/A	42
	CS20	No Documentation Available		
	CS21	No Documentation Available		
1976	CS22	Budweiser Centennial Hofbrau Style	N/A	27
	CS23	No Documentation Available		
	CS24	No Documentation Available		
	CS25	No Documentation Available		
1976	CS26	A&Eagle	N/A	37
1976	CS27	Michelob	N/A	119
1976	CS28	A&Eagle Lidded (reference CSL2)	N/A	36

*A=Available steins as of publication date; N/A=Not available as of publication date

Item Number/Year Index

Item Number/Year Index

Item Number/Year Index

Item Number/Year Index

Item Number/Year Index

Item Number/Year Index

Item Number/Year Index

Item Number/Year Index

Item Number/Year Index

Item Number/Year Index

Alphabetical Index

NOTE: *Several of the Item Numbers were assigned to steins which were in development, yet never produced, and some of the Item Numbers have been assigned to several steins which are currently in production.*

*A=Available steins as of publication date; N/A=Not available as of publication date

Alphabetical Index

Alphabetical Index

Alphabetical Index

Alphabetical Index

Alphabetical Index

Alphabetical Index

Alphabetical Index

Alphabetical Index

Alphabetical Index

Alphabetical Index

☑ STEIN NAME AND ITEM NUMBER:	ISSUE YEAR:	WHERE/WHEN PURCHASED:	AMOUNT PAID:
❏ 50th Anniversary Celebration, CS57	1982	_____	_____
❏ 1984/1985 Christmas Assortment, CS82		_____	_____
❏ 1984 Budweiser Olympic Games, CS60	1984	_____	_____
❏ 1988 Winter Olympic Games Lidded, CS81	1987	_____	_____
❏ 1992 U.S. Olympic Summer Team Lidded, CS163	1992	_____	_____
❏ 1992 U.S. Olympic Winter Team Lidded, CS162	1991	_____	_____
❏ 1993 Budweiser Oktoberfest, CS202	1993	_____	_____
❏ 1996 St. Patrick's Day Horseshoe, CS269	1996	_____	_____
❏ 1996 U.S. Olympic Team Gymnastics Lidded. CS262	1995	_____	_____
❏ 1996 U.S. Olympic Team Track & Field Lidded, CS246	1995	_____	_____
❏ A Perfect Christmas, CS167	1992	_____	_____
❏ A Perfect Christmas – Gold Decal CS167GOLD	1992	_____	_____
❏ A Perfect Christmas – Signature Edition, CS167SE	1992	_____	_____
❏ A&Eagle, CS2	1976	_____	_____
❏ A&Eagle, CS26	1976	_____	_____
❏ A&Eagle Lidded (reference CSL2), CS28	1976	_____	_____
❏ A&Eagle Lidded (reference CS28), CSL2	1976	_____	_____
❏ A&Eagle Logo, CS148	1990	_____	_____
❏ A&Eagle Trademark I (boxed), CS191	1993	_____	_____
❏ A&Eagle Trademark I (with tin), CS201	1992	_____	_____
❏ A&Eagle Trademark II (boxed), CS219	1994	_____	_____
❏ A&Eagle Trademark II (with tin), CS218	1993	_____	_____
❏ A&Eagle Trademark III (boxed), CS240	1995	_____	_____
❏ A&Eagle Trademark III (with tin), CS238	1994	_____	_____
❏ A&Eagle Trademark IV (boxed), CS271	1996	_____	_____
❏ A&Eagle Trademark IV (with tin), CS255	1995	_____	_____
❏ Advertising Through The Decades I 1879-1912, N3989	1992	_____	_____
❏ Advertising Through The Decades II 1905-1914, N3990	1993	_____	_____

✓ STEIN NAME AND ITEM NUMBER:	ISSUE YEAR:	WHERE/WHEN PURCHASED:	AMOUNT PAID:
❏ Advertising Through The Decades III 1911-1915, SO85203	1994		
❏ African Elephant Lidded, CS135	1991		
❏ After The Hunt Lidded, CS155	1991		
❏ Alabama State, SO64282	1992		
❏ Albuquerque Balloon Fiesta: Magic in the Air, N4247	1993		
❏ All I Want For Christmas Lidded, GM13	1994		
❏ America's Favorite Pastime, CS124	1990		
❏ American Bald Eagle Lidded, CS164	1991		
❏ An American Tradition, CS112	1990		
❏ An American Tradition – Gold Decal, CS112GOLD	1990		
❏ An American Tradition – Signature Edition, CS112SE	1990		
❏ Anheuser-Busch Golf Classic: Colorado Easter Seal Society, SO862779	1995		
❏ Anheuser-Busch Recycling: 5 Billion Pounds, SO86266	1995		
❏ Arkansas: Brewed With Rice, N3940	1993		
❏ Arkansas: Rice/Duck, SO51582	1991		
❏ Asian Tiger Lidded, CS126	1990		
❏ Assortment, CS72	N/A		
❏ Athens, New York: Firefighters SO64209	1992		
❏ Bald Eagle Lidded, CS106	1989		
❏ Baseball Mitt, CS244	1995		
❏ Beagle Lidded, CS272	1996		
❏ Berninghaus Lidded, CS105	1990		
❏ Bevo Fox Lidded, CS160	1991		
❏ Billiards, CS278	1996		
❏ Bottled Beer Stein/Tin Set, N3292	1991		
❏ Bottled Treasure, CS193	1993		
❏ Brew House, CS67	1986		
❏ Brew House/Stables Assortment, CS110	N/A		
❏ Bud Dry Logo, CS156	1991		
❏ Bud Label Assortment, CS153	N/A		
❏ Bud Label Assortment, CS172	N/A		
❏ Bud Light Baron, CS61	1983		
❏ Bud Light Logo, CS144	1990		
❏ Bud Man – 1975 Style Lidded, CS1	1975		
❏ Bud Man – 1989 Style Lidded, CS100	1989		
❏ Bud Man – 1993 Style Lidded, CS213	1993		

☑ STEIN NAME AND ITEM NUMBER:	ISSUE YEAR:	WHERE/WHEN PURCHASED:	AMOUNT PAID:
❑ Budweiser 1992 U.S. Olympic Team, CS168	1991	_____	_____
❑ Budweiser Antique Label, CS127	1990	_____	_____
❑ Budweiser Atlanta 1996 Olympic Games, CS249	1996	_____	_____
❑ Budweiser Burns Coal, SO64374	1992	_____	_____
❑ Budweiser Bottled Beer, CS136	1991	_____	_____
❑ Budweiser Brickyard 400: Inaugural Race, N4822	1994	_____	_____
❑ Budweiser Brickyard 400, N5359	1995	_____	_____
❑ Budweiser California, CS56	1981	_____	_____
❑ Budweiser Centennial, CS13	1976	_____	_____
❑ Budweiser Centennial Hofbrau Style, CS22	1976	_____	_____
❑ Budweiser Centennial Lidded, CSL7	1976	_____	_____
❑ Budweiser Champion Clydesdales, CS19	1980	_____	_____
❑ Budweiser Champion Clydesdales, CS19A	1981	_____	_____
❑ Budweiser Chicago Skyline, CS40	1980	_____	_____
❑ Budweiser Chicagoland, CS51	1981	_____	_____
❑ Budweiser Chip Hanauer, N5511	1995	_____	_____
❑ Budweiser Clydesdales at the Bauernhof Lidded, CB1	1995	_____	_____
❑ Budweiser Field & Stream Set, CS95	1988	_____	_____
❑ Bud-weis-er Frogs, N5402	1995	_____	_____
❑ Budweiser Golf Bag, CS225	1994	_____	_____
❑ Budweiser Hofbrau Style, CS46	1980	_____	_____
❑ Budweiser Kenny Bernstein, N5512	1995	_____	_____
❑ Budweiser Ken Schrader, N5054	1995	_____	_____
❑ Budweiser Ken Schrader, N5510	1995	_____	_____
❑ Budweiser Label, CS18	1976	_____	_____
❑ Budweiser Label – 1989, CS101	1989	_____	_____
❑ Budweiser Label – 1996, CS282	1996	_____	_____
❑ Budweiser Logo, CS143	1990	_____	_____
❑ Budweiser Oktoberfest, CS185	1992	_____	_____
❑ Budweiser Pewter Lidded, N2755	1991	_____	_____
❑ Budweiser Racing (reference N3553), SO63790	1992	_____	_____
❑ Budweiser Racing (reference SO63790), N3553	1992	_____	_____
❑ Budweiser Rodeo, CS184	1992	_____	_____
❑ Budweiser Rodeo, N5205	1995	_____	_____
❑ Budweiser San Francisco, CS59	1983	_____	_____
❑ Budweiser Salutes the			

☑ STEIN NAME AND ITEM NUMBER:	ISSUE YEAR:	WHERE/WHEN PURCHASED:	AMOUNT PAID:
Air Force, CS228	1994		
❏ Budweiser Salutes the Army, CS224	1994		
❏ Budweiser Salutes the Marines, CS256	1995		
❏ Budweiser Salutes the Navy, CS243	1995		
❏ Budweiser Summer Olympic Games, CS92	1988		
❏ Budweiser Summer Olympic Games Lidded, CS91	1988		
❏ Budweiser Stables, CS73	1987		
❏ Budweiser Texas, CS52	1981		
❏ Budweiser Winter Olympic Games, CS85	1988		
❏ Budweiser's Greatest Triumph Lidded, CS222	1994		
❏ Adolphus Busch Lidded , CS216	1993		
❏ Adolphus Busch Lidded, N/A	N/A		
❏ Adolphus Busch III Lidded, CS265	1995		
❏ August A. Busch, Sr. Lidded, CS229	1994		
❏ Busch Gardens Extinction is Forever I	1985		
❏ Busch Gardens Extinction is Forever II, BG1	1990		
❏ Busch Gardens Extinction is Forever III, BG2	1992		
❏ Busch Hofbrau Style, CS44	1980		
❏ Busch Logo, CS147	1990		
❏ California: Big Bear Oktoberfest 20th Anniversary, SO49433	1990		
❏ California: Big Bear Oktoberfest 21st Anniversary, SO53954	1991		
❏ California: Big Bear Oktoberfest 25th Anniversary, SO86916	1995		
❏ Cameo Wheatland, CS58	1983		
❏ Canteen Decanter Set Lidded, CS36	1976		
❏ Cardinals: 100th Anniversary, N3767	1992		
❏ Centennial Olympic Games Giftware, CS266	1995		
❏ Centennial Olympic Games Premier Edition Lidded, CS267	1996		
❏ Center Ice, CS209	1993		
❏ Chaldean & Ohio: Hammurabi King of Mesopotamia, SO862781	1995		
❏ Chasing The Checkered Flag, CS132	1991		
❏ Cherub Lidded, CS182	1992		
❏ Chiefs of Police: 100th Anniversary, N3589	1993		
❏ Cincinnati: Tallstacks, N3942	1992		

✓ STEIN NAME AND ITEM NUMBER:	ISSUE YEAR:	WHERE/WHEN PURCHASED:	AMOUNT PAID:
❏ Classic I Lidded, CS93	1988	_____	_____
❏ Classic II Lidded, CS104	1989	_____	_____
❏ Classic III Lidded, CS113	1990	_____	_____
❏ Classic IV Lidded, CS130	1991	_____	_____
❏ Clydesdale Mare & Foal, CS90	1988	_____	_____
❏ Clydesdale Decanter Lidded, CS33	1976	_____	_____
❏ Clydesdales Assortment, CS123	N/A	_____	_____
❏ Clydesdales Assortment, CS154	N/A	_____	_____
❏ Clydesdales, CS12	1976	_____	_____
❏ Clydesdales, CS15	1976	_____	_____
❏ Clydesdales Lidded, CSL29	1976	_____	_____
❏ Clydesdales Lidded, CSL9	1976	_____	_____
❏ Clydesdales On Parade, CS161	1992	_____	_____
❏ Clydesdales Training Hitch, CS131	1991	_____	_____
❏ Cobblestone Passage, CS88	1988	_____	_____
❏ Colorado, SO86539	1995	_____	_____
❏ Colorado: And No Place Else, SO52848	1991	_____	_____
❏ Colorado Ducks Unlimited Series: Goose Lidded, SO86531	1995	_____	_____
❏ Colorado Ducks Unlimited Series: Mallard Lidded, N4252	1993	_____	_____
❏ Colorado Ducks Unlimited Series: Wood Duck Lidded, N4998	1994	_____	_____
❏ Columbian Exposition Lidded, CS169	1992	_____	_____
❏ Coracao Decanter Set, CS31	1976	_____	_____
❏ Cougar Lidded, CS253	1995	_____	_____
❏ Covered Bridge, CS62	1984	_____	_____
❏ Cowboy Boot, CS251	1994	_____	_____
❏ Daytona: Bud Bike Week, N/A	1990	_____	_____
❏ Daytona: Bud Speed Week, N/A	1990	_____	_____
❏ Discover America Assortment, CS178	N/A	_____	_____
❏ Dodge City Days, SO53465	1991	_____	_____
❏ Dolphin Lidded, CS187	1992	_____	_____
❏ Du Quoin: State Fair, N3941	1992	_____	_____
❏ Bill Elliott Lidded, CS196	1993	_____	_____
❏ Bill Elliott Lidded – Signature Edition, CS196SE	1993	_____	_____
❏ Erin Go Bud, CS109	1991	_____	_____
❏ Faust Beer, SO94855	1995	_____	_____
❏ Flatwall Assortment, CS149	N/A	_____	_____
❏ Fort Lewis, Washington, SO54147	1991	_____	_____
❏ Ganymede Lidded, CS190	1993	_____	_____

☑ STEIN NAME AND ITEM NUMBER:	ISSUE YEAR:	WHERE/WHEN PURCHASED:	AMOUNT PAID:
❏ General Assortment, CS116	N/A		
❏ Georgia: Bass, SO63840	1992		
❏ Georgia: Deer, SO64054	1992		
❏ Georgia Fishing: On My Mind, SO53834	1991		
❏ Georgia Hunting: On My Mind SO54141	1991		
❏ German Pilique, CS5	1975		
❏ German Pilique Lidded, CSL5	1976		
❏ German Tavern Scene, CS4	1976		
❏ German Tavern Scene Lidded, CSL6	1975		
❏ German Wine Set, CS32	1976		
❏ Giant Panda Lidded, CS173	1992		
❏ Giant Panda Lidded, GM8	1995		
❏ Golden Retriever Lidded, GM2	1993		
❏ Golden Retriever Lidded, CS248	1995		
❏ General Ulysses S. Grant Lidded, CS181	1992		
❏ Grant's Cabin, CS83	1988		
❏ Grant's Cabin/Old Schoolhouse 2-Pack Assortment, CS111	N/A		
❏ Grant's Farm Gates, CS70	1987		
❏ Gray Wolf Lidded, CS226	1994		
❏ Great Horned Owl Lidded, CS264	1995		
❏ Great White Shark Lidded, CS247	1995		
❏ Grizzly Bear Lidded, CS199	1993		
❏ Heroes Of The Hardwood, CS134	1991		
❏ Historical Assortment, CS121	N/A		
❏ Holanda Decanter Set: Antique Brown, CS34	1976		
❏ Holanda Decanter Set: Blue, CS35	1976		
❏ Hometown Holiday , CS211	1994		
❏ Hometown Holiday - Gold Decal, CS211GOLD	1994		
❏ Hometown Holiday - Signature Edition Lidded, CS211SE	1994		
❏ Horse Harness, CS94	1988		
❏ Horsehead, CS76	1987		
❏ Horsehead, CS78	1987		
❏ Horseshoe Assortment, CS122	N/A		
❏ Horseshoe, CS68	1986		
❏ Horseshoe, CS77	1987		
❏ Houston: Rodeo, N/A	1991		
❏ Houston: Texas Pride, SO86865	1995		

☑ STEIN NAME AND ITEM NUMBER:	ISSUE YEAR:	WHERE/WHEN PURCHASED:	AMOUNT PAID:
❏ Idaho: Centennial, SO49804	1990		
❏ Illinois Sportsmen, N4241	1993		
❏ Illinois State, SO54808	1991		
❏ Indiana: Crossroads Of America, SO68206	1992		
❏ Indiana Hoosier Hysteria, N4242	1993		
❏ Introduction to Wisconsin Wildlife Series: Duck, N/A	1990		
❏ Introductory Assortment, CS117	N/A		
❏ Introductory Assortment, CS150	N/A		
❏ Introductory Assortment, CS175	N/A		
❏ Iowa: The Time Is Right, SO67816	1992		
❏ It's A Bud Thing, N3645	1992		
❏ Kansas: Good To Know You, SO53618	1991		
❏ Katakombe, CS3	1976		
❏ Katakombe Lidded, CSL3	1976		
❏ John F. Kennedy Lidded, GM4	1993		
❏ Kentucky: The Celebration, SO54022	1991		
❏ Killer Whale Lidded, CS186	1992		
❏ King–A Regal Spirit Lidded, CB4	1996		
❏ King Cobra, CS80	1987		
❏ Labrador Lidded, CS195	1993		
❏ Labrador Lidded, GM17	1996		
❏ General Robert E. Lee Lidded, CS188	1993		
❏ Lighting the Way Home, CS263	1995		
❏ Lighting the Way Home - Gold Decal, CS263GOLD	1995		
❏ Lighting the Way Home - Signature Edition Lidded, CS263SE	1995		
❏ Limited Edition Assortment, CS120	N/A		
❏ Limited Edition I Lidded, CS64	1985		
❏ Limited Edition II Lidded, CS65	1986		
❏ Limited Edition III Lidded, CS71	1987		
❏ Limited Edition IV Lidded, CS75	1988		
❏ Limited Edition V Lidded, CS98	1989		
❏ Abraham Lincoln Lidded, CS189	1993		
❏ Logo Assortment, CS180	N/A		
❏ Joe Louis Lidded, CS206	1993		
❏ Louisiana: We're Really Cookin' SO67814	1992		
❏ Luck O' The Irish, CS210	1994		
❏ Mallard Lidded, GM7	1994		
❏ Manatee Lidded, CS203	1994		

☑ STEIN NAME AND ITEM NUMBER:	ISSUE YEAR:	WHERE/WHEN PURCHASED:	AMOUNT PAID:
❏ *Mardi Gras 1993, N4073*	1993		
❏ *Mardi Gras 1994, N4467*	1994		
❏ *Mardi Gras 1995, SO86277*	1995		
❏ *Mardi Gras: Bud Mardi Gras '92, SO56219*	1992		
❏ *Mardi Gras: Nothing Beats A Bud, SO50500*	1991		
❏ *Michelob, CS27*	1976		
❏ *Michelob Dry Logo, CS146*	1990		
❏ *Michelob Dry Pewter Lidded, N2371*	1991		
❏ *Michelob Hofbrau Style, CS45*	1980		
❏ *Michelob Logo, CS145*	1990		
❏ *Michelob Pewter Lidded, CS158*	1991		
❏ *Michigan: 12th World Hot Air Balloon Championship, SO86475*	1995		
❏ *Michigan Ducks Unlimited Series: Duck Lidded, SO42208*	1990		
❏ *Michigan Ducks Unlimited Series: Gadwell Duck, N4903S*	1994		
❏ *Michigan Ducks Unlimited Series: Heron Lidded, N4251*	1993		
❏ *Michigan Ducks Unlimited Series: Loon Lidded, SO54807*	1991		
❏ *Michigan Ducks Unlimited Series: Swan Lidded, N3828*	1992		
❏ *Michigan Ducks Unlimited Wholesaler Series: Duck Lidded, SO64169*	1992		
❏ *Mini Mug Set Of Four, CS8*	N/A		
❏ *Minnesota Wildlife Series: Canada Geese, N4250*	1993		
❏ *Minnesota Wildlife Series: Loon SO53143*	1991		
❏ *Minnesota Wildlife Series: Mallard SO67817*	1992		
❏ *Minnesota Wildlife Series: Pheasants SO86279*	1995		
❏ *Mirror of Truth Lidded, CS252*	1995		
❏ *Mississippi Bass: Always In Season SO54822*	1991		
❏ *Mississippi Deer: Always In Season SO54806*	1991		
❏ *Missouri: Always in Season, N4118*	1993		
❏ *Missouri: Wake Up To Missouri, SO54149*	1991		
❏ *National Hobo Convention, SO84670*	1994		
❏ *Natural Light, CS9*	1977		
❏ *Natural Light Hofbrau Style, CS43*	1980		

☑ STEIN NAME AND ITEM NUMBER:	ISSUE YEAR:	WHERE/WHEN PURCHASED:	AMOUNT PAID:
❏ Nebraska Ducks Unlimited Series: Goose Lidded, SO86532	1995		
❏ Nebraska: Traditions, SO50512	1991		
❏ Nebraska: Wildlife, N4117	1993		
❏ New York: A State of Mind, SO54214	1991		
❏ New York State II, SO67694	1992		
❏ Nina Lidded, CS107	1990		
❏ North Carolina: Carolina On My Mind, SO64215	1992		
❏ North/South Dakota, SO42268	1989		
❏ O'Doul's: What Beer Drinkers Drink (reference N3522D), N3522	1992		
❏ O'Doul's: What Beer Drinkers Drink (reference N3522), N3522D	1992		
❏ Official 1994 World Cup Commemorative Lidded, CS230	1994		
❏ Official Centennial Olympic Games Lidded, CS259	1995		
❏ Ohio Jaycees: Partners in Leadership Development, N4119	1993		
❏ Ohio Sportsmen, SO862780	1995		
❏ Ohio: The Heart Of It All, SO55446	1991		
❏ Oklahoma: Better Sooner Than Later, SO53689	1991		
❏ Oklahoma: Festival Of The Horse, SO55447	1991		
❏ Oktoberfest, SO54077	1991		
❏ Oktoberfest Busch Gardens, CS42	1980		
❏ Old School House, CS84	1988		
❏ Olympic Assortment, CS96	N/A		
❏ Osprey Lidded, CS212	1994		
❏ Par For The Course, CS165	1992		
❏ Parade Dress, CS99	1989		
❏ Pennsylvania: A State For All Seasons, SO54215	1991		
❏ Peregrine Falcon Lidded, CS183	1992		
❏ Phoenix: One Million Barrels, N4105	1993		
❏ Pinta Lidded, CS129	1991		
❏ Pointer Lidded, GM16	1995		
❏ Post Convention-Heritage: Adolphus Busch, CS87	1988		
❏ Post Convention-Heritage: Adolphus Busch III, CS114	1989		
❏ Post Convention-Heritage: August Busch Jr., CS141	1990		
❏ Post Convention-Heritage: August Busch Sr., CS102	1988		

☑ STEIN NAME AND ITEM NUMBER:	ISSUE YEAR:	WHERE/WHEN PURCHASED:	AMOUNT PAID:
❏ Post Convention-Heritage: August Busch III, CS174	1991		
❏ Post Convention-Olympic, CS53	1982		
❏ Post Convention-Olympic, CS54	1982		
❏ Post Convention-Olympic, CS55	1982		
❏ Pot of Gold, CS166	1992		
❏ Program Assortment, CS152	N/A		
❏ Program Assortment, CS177	N/A		
❏ Proud and Free, CS223	1994		
❏ Puerto Rico: Quinto Centenario, SO65691	1992		
❏ Racing Team, CS194	1993		
❏ Redlands: Chili Cook-Off, SO53757	1991		
❏ Rosie the Riveter Lidded, GM9	1995		
❏ Rumble on the River: 12th Annual, SO86506	1995		
❏ Babe Ruth Lidded, CS142	1991		
❏ San Antonio: Fiesta, SO52190	1991		
❏ Santa Maria Lidded, CS138	1992		
❏ Santa's Helper Lidded, GM3	1993		
❏ Santa's Mailbag Lidded, GM1	1992		
❏ "Saturday Evening Post" Christmas Lidded, GL5	1995		
❏ Save The Bay I, SO52286	1991		
❏ Save The Bay II, N4120	1993		
❏ Save The Lake Pontchartrain, SO54240	1991		
❏ Seattle: Good Will Games, SO47627	1990		
❏ Senior Grande , CS6	1977		
❏ Senior Grande Lidded, CSL4	1975		
❏ Setter Lidded, CS205	1994		
❏ Six Pack Mini Steins, N3289	1992		
❏ Six Pack II Mini Steins, N4571	1995		
❏ Snow Capped Mountains, CS63	1985		
❏ Snowy Woodland, CS50	1981		
❏ Special Delivery, CS192	1993		
❏ Special Delivery – Gold Decal, CS192GOLD	1993		
❏ Special Delivery – Signature Edition, CS192SE	1993		
❏ Spencer Gifts' Christmas Meeting: Sea World, N3264	1995		
❏ Sports History Assortment, CS179	N/A		
❏ Springer Spaniel Lidded, GM5	1994		

✔ STEIN NAME AND ITEM NUMBER:	ISSUE YEAR:	WHERE/WHEN PURCHASED:	AMOUNT PAID:
❏ St. Louis Cardinals Lidded, CS125	1989	_____	_____
❏ St. Louis Decanter, CS37	1976	_____	_____
❏ St. Louis Decanter Set, CS38	1976	_____	_____
❏ St. Nick, CS79	1987	_____	_____
❏ Temecula: Tractor Race, SO53847	1991	_____	_____
❏ Tennessee, SO85008	1995	_____	_____
❏ Tennessee: We're Playing Your Song, SO63887	1992	_____	_____
❏ Texas: Living Free In Texas (reference SO64487), N3648	1992	_____	_____
❏ Texas: Living Free In Texas (reference N3648), SO64487	1992	_____	_____
❏ The Brew House Clock Tower Lidded, CB2	1995	_____	_____
❏ The Dugout Lidded, GL1	1993	_____	_____
❏ The Season's Best, CS133	1991	_____	_____
❏ The Season's Best – Gold Decal, CS133GOLD	1991	_____	_____
❏ The Season's Best – Signature Edition, CS133SE	1991	_____	_____
❏ Jim Thorpe Lidded, CS171	1992	_____	_____
❏ Tip O' The Hat , CS242	1995	_____	_____
❏ Traditional House , CS66	1986	_____	_____
❏ Triple Self-Portrait Lidded, GM6	1994	_____	_____
❏ U.S. Bicentennial, CS14	1976	_____	_____
❏ U.S. Bicentennial Lidded, CSL8	1976	_____	_____
❏ United States JCI Senate, SO82138	1994	_____	_____
❏ United Way 1993 Fair Share, N4121	1993	_____	_____
❏ United Way 1994 Fair Share Lidded, SO84542	1994	_____	_____
❏ Utah: Naturally, SO52847	1991	_____	_____
❏ Variety Assortment, CS118	N/A	_____	_____
❏ Variety Assortment, CS151	N/A	_____	_____
❏ Variety Assortment, CS176	N/A	_____	_____
❏ Vermont: Bicentennial, SO53758	1991	_____	_____
❏ West Texas: Centennial, N3943	1992	_____	_____
❏ Winchester Lidded, GL2	1994	_____	_____
❏ Winchester Model 94 Lidded, GM10	1994	_____	_____
❏ Winter Evening, CS89	1989	_____	_____
❏ Wisconsin: Vince Lombardi Lidded, N4249	1993	_____	_____
❏ Wisconsin: Waterfowl - Gold Lid, N4248G	1993	_____	_____
❏ Wisconsin: Waterfowl - Pewter Lid,			

☑ STEIN NAME AND ITEM NUMBER:	ISSUE YEAR:	WHERE/WHEN PURCHASED:	AMOUNT PAID:
N4248P	1993		
❏ Wisconsin Wildlife Series: Best Beer-Best Deer Lidded, SO55713	1991		
❏ Wisconsin Wildlife Series: Deer, SO49700	1990		
❏ Wisconsin Wildlife Series: Duck, SO49699	1990		
❏ Wisconsin Wildlife Series: Turkey, SO48249	1990		
❏ Wisconsin Wildlife Series: Walleye, SO49244	1990		
❏ World Cup USA '94: Boston, N4559	1994		
❏ World Cup USA '94: Chicago, N4563	1994		
❏ World Cup USA '94: Dallas, N4565	1994		
❏ World Cup USA '94: Detroit, N4561	1994		
❏ World Cup USA '94: Los Angeles, N4558	1994		
❏ World Cup USA '94: New York/New Jersey, N4560	1994		
❏ World Cup USA '94: Orlando, N4564	1994		
❏ World Cup USA '94: San Francisco, N4562	1994		
❏ World Cup USA '94: Washington D.C., N4566	1994		
❏ World Famous Clydesdales, CS74	1987		
❏ World's Largest Brewer, CB3	1996		
❏ Würzburger, CS39	Circa 1979		
❏ Wyoming: Centennial A, SO49243	1990		
❏ Wyoming: Centennial B, SO50138	1990		
❏ Other			
❏ Other			
❏ Other			
❏ Other			
❏ Other			
❏ Other			
❏ Other			
❏ Other			
❏ Other			
❏ Other			
❏ Other			
❏ Other			

Secondary Market Information

Values of Anheuser-Busch steins can escalate over time—often very quickly. A few examples of this fact are shown at right, as listed by the Collectors' Information Bureau. Of particular note is our Endangered Species Series' Bald Eagle Stein, valued at over ten times its original price, and our 1993 Signature Edition Holiday Stein, which doubled in value in less than two years.

The Collectors' Information Bureau's annual "Collectibles Market Guide and Price Index"—and its mid-year update—are recognized as the authoritative guides to secondary market values for a wide variety of limited-edition collectibles, including steins. The Bureau establishes a value range for each item based on input from a panel of experts located across the United States.

The guide can be found at libraries, book stores and some dealers, and can be purchased from the Bureau by calling 708-842-2200, or writing 5065 Shoreline Road, Suite 200, Barrington, IL 60010.

Prices quoted are only estimates by an independent source. Anheuser-Busch is not responsible for and makes no guarantees of future value.

Senior Grande
ITEM NUMBER:
CS6 – Retired
ISSUE YEAR/PRICE:
1975 / Not available
BUREAU'S QUOTE:
$600-$750

Snowy Woodland
ITEM NUMBER:
CS50 – Retired
ISSUE YEAR/PRICE:
1981/$9.95
BUREAU'S QUOTE:
$195-$275

Budweiser Field & Stream Set
ITEM NUMBER:
CS95 – Retired
ISSUE YEAR/PRICE:
1988/$69.95
BUREAU'S QUOTE:
$200-$250

Bald Eagle
ITEM NUMBER:
CS106 – Retired
ISSUE YEAR/PRICE:
1989/$24.95
BUREAU'S QUOTE:
$250-$300

Special Delivery Signature Edition
ITEM NUMBER:
CS192SE – Retired
ISSUE YEAR/PRICE:
1993/$60.00
BUREAU'S QUOTE:
$100-$125